# INNOCENCE
# TO
# EVIL

# VOLUME I

## INNOCENCE TO EVIL
*First Edition*

This book is based on true stories and true events.

### WRITTEN BY ANTHONY. J. ALLAN

COPYRIGHT 2004 ANTHONY ALLAN
www.innocencetoevil.co.uk

First published in Great Britain in September 2004
By JUNAL

Cover Design: Bargates Print • www.bargates.com

Printed by Antony Rowe Ltd, Chippenham, Wiltshire

# FOREWORD

In most cases the majority of people would give up mentally when things seem to get heavy and become intolerable. The idea of suicide or having a breakdown seems a natural reaction to life when it is not worth living. The only time life is not worth living is when you yourself determine that time has come but remember, that is your assumption.

Reacting in a strange way alien to your own feelings is your way of shouting out at the world. Who ever said the world is a fair place to live in? Who ever said life was beautiful?

If you cannot fight your way through the most stressful times in life it means you have become disillusioned, because there is a way through everything and every situation, no matter what you are up against.

We all have the power within ourselves to march on; it's just that we don't get taught that until later on in life. It is something called self-belief, you must believe in yourself and determine that there is always a way through, no matter how dark life becomes.

Hope is the answer even if there is none.
Parents and guardians hold our hands for a short part of life
But carry us in their hearts forever.

# CHAPTER ONE
# THE LOCAL

It was a cool summer evening, the day was fading away. The skyline drifting into a blood red darkness. There was a strange and almost callous air in the atmosphere, not like the usual jovial jest that you only seem to experience in the local pubs of Liverpool. There was something going on, something...

A group were sitting at a table by the poolroom, planning, scheming, up to some skulduggery. Why not? They were the boy's they were the main men, the firm. Some young kid had not long been living in the area, he was from Page Moss, the other side of Huyton and he was in their pub that very night. So, he had refused to borrow them his car to do a bit of work in (work to them meant a bit of graft, a job, stealing, robbing etc).

He had to pay. In fact this firm had to show that when asked to do something it had to be done, they won't and cannot tolerate young kids saying no. This kid who just happened to be at the bar with his old man was getting up their noses. Fact was they knew nothing of this kid, nothing about him at all.

The bar was quite busy as usual and the music was up high, the beers were flowing, definitely good for business. One of the firm edged his way to the bar, a couple of others slowly made their way around the bar but, in a slippery way nodding out to fellow members that it was about to go off. The main man or shall we refer to him as the hero, the boy, the governor...I don't quite know how to refer to him so, as with all dead hard gobshites that love to bully, I shall name him the "nob".

Well, he makes his order at the bar for sixteen pints of lager. Now considering there is only a handful in his company it appears he needs time to adjust and compose himself, maybe buying time awaiting a nod. A comment was made in a friendly fashion as to someone must be a thirsty chap. Low and behold its only the young kids dad, the one who wouldn't lend his car out to their firm. Do we need any more abuse from these people? A sneaky smile was in retort until the old man turned to his other side.

He could not tell the old man or his son they were in the bad books. No. Definitely not. Well, they might face him and even have the arse-hole to fight back. Now hold on a minute, it could be that he may have come a cropper. After all the old man was passed it and the kid was just old enough to get in the pub, I mean he actually looked Eighteen with the build of a stick insect, all nine stone of him. Now that to me must be so menacing that the only thing to do is steal it. What else can a big time plastic gangster twenty-eight years old, in the prime of his life do?

Nothing else for it then. The nob lines the old man up, looks for the nods. He gets the ok. He makes sure his prey is not looking in his direction, all clear. One step, two step... Crack!! Right into the side of the old mans temple. He used his whole weight and body strength behind this one. Oh! Did he connect? Bingo! This had to be the mother of mothers. What a punch. This is it, the moment of truth, the glory was about to be his. Behold the king is in town with his merry men. What a Star.

The old man was drinking his pint at the bar, long day at work. Straight work. He enjoyed his pint after work and just as he raised the glass, Crack!! His head wobbled to the right, yet he tried not to fall and stood in shock for a few seconds trying to come to terms with why his world just went seriously wrong. Why should it be wobbled? What happened?

The young kid was drinking away chatting to his dad and uncle when a fist comes flashing across the face of his father. Shock was tonic of the day. How? Why? What the fuck!! He turned and managed to mutter something about that being his dad, that's when he realised he was going backwards under a hail of punches. It had to stop. It did when his back was to reach the wall as he could not go back no more.

His senses came to him and his instant reaction

was a bodily one. Bang, bang, bang, out came a rage with a volley of punches and the forward motion showed he had turned the onslaught around and was speedily getting on top. As people gathered around, legs, feet and fists were being dished to the young kid as he seemed to be on top getting the better of his attacker. It did not get much further as the landlord decided that it was to be stopped.

The young lad was barred from the pub. After all the cheeky little fella had the audacity to fight back. The young lad was fuming, he was going ape shit. Three of the lads stood outside the door and tried to tell him it was a family thing, they were all related and basically they were the firm not to be fucked with as they ran Huyton, so they claimed.

The front door of the pub peaked open about an inch, time to steal another one eh? The nob sprung out the door fist first, the young kid side stepped it and followed up with a string of head punches. As they connected, the three so called relatives steamed in to the young kid. He scrambled out of it and stood there and swore it's not over. The nob was told to come outside to finish it but apparently had other things to do, probably visiting the toilet, who knows?

That night the nob had a visit at his front door. It was the young kid wanting to level it out and have a one to one, the nob declined the invitation, some words were exchanged about stealing it and how it was a low thing to do, a very dirty and sly way to fight.

Next morning the nob was given another visit, the young kid had his face marked up and told him straight, that if he did not come out and face him one to one, he would not let it go. The nob declined, it was the final invitation. In football terms after two yellow cards, the red follows and we all know what that means. Off!

It seemed that there would never be a fair fight as the only time the nob came out or travelled anywhere he was firm handed or surrounded in the safety of the pub. It got to the point where the only way a fight could happen would be if it was at the pub with his back up, he could not fight on his own he needed his audience in case it went wrong. What a man.

There were several incidents that followed where there was confrontations on the streets but there was always a few others wanting to get involved, it gave the nob a sense of being a someone and he really gloated, in a bitter laughing and taunting way. He wanted the world to know how hard he was and continued to rub it in.

The nob made threats as to finish the kid's family off and blow them all away. Everything he said that he was going to do, to every member of the kid's family seemed to hit a raw nerve. The kid took the threats as serious. He worried about the threats and they played on his mind, after all to a young kid it must have seemed like the end of the world for plastic gangsters to be all out to get him. It became a serious situation.

# CHAPTER TWO
# ROBBERY OF THE SEAWEED

A few months later some 250 miles south, in the town of Southampton, last orders at the bar had been called and the last of the local punter's were leaving. There was the publican, his wife and the barmaid cleaning up and locking the doors. Must get ready for tomorrow. An hour later all is done and its that time again, bed.

They were all sleeping except for the three men on the flat roof adjacent to the pub, they were going to a party all dressed for the occasion and boy oh boy, was they about to have a party! They were all in fancy dress, Number One was dressed in dark clothes wearing gloves and a full-face balaclava with only two slits to see from. No mouth or ears visible.

Yes, he was about to start the party and invite himself in the pub through the window head first as scary person Number One. Behind him was scary person Number Two, dressed again in dark clothes with a woolly hat and scarf to match. Scary person Number Three was also dressed as the others in dark clothes, this one was determined to steal the show, his fancy dress head piece was a pair of women's tights, pulled tight over his head. Close to looking like a cunt, literally.

The Three party poopers had not been given invites and had not even let the manager know that they would be using the pub as their venue. I think they were intent on having a surprise fancy dress party. They clearly intended to have their way and brought along with them some incentive just to inspire the occupants of the pub, a nine-inch kitchen knife, a nasty looking meat cleaver and a lead cosh, by the way the cleaver was as sharp as a razor.

The final minutes out on the roof were spent assuring each other as to who went where and who done what. The cleaver was not to be exposed unless emergency called for it. The difference being about ten years. You see if it was to be used it would take a life in one foul swipe. Murder or serious injury like limbs lost means the big boys get involved and high-ranking detectives will deal with the crime and they are dedicated to that particular offence.

Just a plain Robbery will mean the local C.I.D. get involved and have to deal with it. They are not as high up and have fewer resources open to them to catch any villains. The local C.I.D. are not very feared by the modern criminals of today's world.

They went over it again and clarified every move

that they could possibly encounter when they went in. They had watched the pub and had cased it for a week, they knew the takings would be in the bank the next morning. Tonight was the perfect time to hit it, they were sure and had all agreed to it.

They counted to three and in they went. Party time! One, Two and Three went literally head first through the biggest window not even smashing the glass first, just diving straight through. Crash! Went the window and all three almost piled on top of each other. It seems it was an unused bedroom or someone was up and about.

They made for the doorway lit up by the landing light. Secure all bodies, secure the doors and then search the whole place, that was their drill. These boys were professional at this and knew how to move fast and do their business. This was a job to be carried out with military precision. Within seconds they had it all secure.

Number One hit the master bedroom with a controlled, no fucking about attitude, it was what he was good at. He ran straight into the master room, a woman lay naked not quite asleep and began to move out of the bed. The manager was half way out of his bed, he was not small. He was six foot three and was weighing in at around twenty-two stone, more like a scrum half rugby player in size. Number One liked a challenge and directed his full attention the manager's way. He smashed him straight into the face and head with a sickening fury, the thuds and squelches from the blows were sickening.

It all stopped suddenly and as cold as you like Number One told him in a mild manner to do what he is told and no one would get hurt. Now you got to remember this guy is half way into a coma bleeding like a squashed tomato, he was looking more like the Elephant man as the seconds went by. This man was not about to argue with a mouse.

The two women were now present in the master room, they were ordered to put on clothes. When the women were decent they were tied up with rope, hands behind their backs and feet together, very secure. The manager was tied up and was trying to speak but only muffles and groans could be heard, not to mention his jaw was shattered and he would be needing some serious medical attention. Number One did not fuck about.

The pub was searched by Number Three whilst, One and Two stood over the victims. They were very polite and helpful to the party poopers, they told them where all the money was. Not to convinced that all the money and jewellery had been collected, Number Two decided to leave the room and returned seconds later with a container.

He told One and Three to move the women out the way, flicked the lid off the container and poured the fluid all over the manager slowly and dramatically whilst staring at the women. Number One spoke to the women whilst pulling a lighter from his pocket. He didn't have to say too much as the women had their own thoughts.

One of the woman fainted and the other collapsed into a heap begging for mercy. They must have thought the manager was about to turn into Guy Fawkes or a ball of fire, either way she told them there was another few grand hidden under a floorboard.

All three occupants of the pub were laid bounded on the bed and warned not to move, the three party animals disappeared into the night. The victims waited for a short time, struggled free and called nine, nine, nine. They required the police and an ambulance immediately.

# DEATH THREAT TERROR OF PUB FAMILY

NIGHTMARE ORDEAL: Brutally beaten Ronald Bannister and his wife Sara

## Brutal raiders pounce

A huge police hunt is on throughout the south for a murderous gang of burglars who threatened to burn a family to death in a Southampton pub today.

The death threat came during a merciless raid for £3,000 cash and £3,000 worth of jewellery.

Vicious masked raiders smashed their way into the Seaweed Inn, Weston Lane, at about 1.30am.

They clubbed landlord Ronald Bannister (43) senseless as he lay half-asleep in his bed.

They held knives to the backs of his wife Sara and live-in barmaid Yvonne Cameron.

They left four-year-old George Bannister sitting weeping amongst a litter of broken glass.

They hooded the two women

### REPORT from MARY ACKROYD

with pillow cases and tied them together.

And they poured liquid over the backs of all three adults, shouting and screaming: "We'll set you on fire if you don't say where the money is..

This is the way 34-year-old Sara Bannister recalled the horror of the ordeal:

"We went to bed about 12.30. The next thing I heard was a tremendous crash. I didn't know what it was. I leapt out of bed.

"Within seconds there were two men in the room, one either side of the bed. The one my side had a knife and put it to my back.

"The other man had a big stick in his hand. They started

shouting and screaming they wanted the money.

"I was desperately trying to wake Ron up but he was deeply asleep. Because he wouldn't answer, the man just picked up the stick and bashed him straight over the head.

"The next thing was that Yvonne was brought into the room by another man.

"We were thrown onto the bed with our heads down. They kept shouting and screaming where's the money, where's the money.

"They asked Ron where the safe was but he was half-senseless by then. So they just hit him and hit him.

"I was so frightened I told them where the safe was. I took them downstairs. I told

them there was money in the tills. Then they asked where the personal money was.

"They said: 'We know you publicans. You've got money.'

"Then they proceeded to pour some sort of liquid down our backs which we assumed was petrol, and said if you don't tell us we will set you alight.

"They ransacked the room and found some money belonging to us. At this point I wondered what had happened to our son, but there was nothing I could do.

"They stuffed pillow cases over my head and Yvonne's. They tied us up together. They took jewellery and after that ransacked through the house.

"They asked if there was anyone else in.

● Turn to page 21.

# Pub raid terror ordeal

■ From page one.

"I said I had a four-year-old son. One of them said he had a four-year-old too and they wouldn't hurt our boy.

"They said if we moved within half-an-hour they would come back and blast us out of the house. We lay there for about 20 minutes too frightened to move, with Ron out cold and bleeding ..."

Ron Bannister, landlord at the Ship Inn, Winchester, until a month ago, hugged the wife he described as "very courageous" and managed to joke about the awful injuries to his face that needed hospital treatment.

"Even though my smile is a bit crooked, we are glad to be still alive, we are well and we still love people," he said.

"I feel sorry for men who can sink to such depths. As I lay there I heard one of them say: 'Let her see the blood on him, that'll make her talk.'

"I've been all over the

"I've been all over the world but this was, arguably, the most frightening thing of my life."

As the huge police hunt began, Detective Inspector John Phillips, of Bitterne CID, appealed for information from anyone who saw or heard "anything untoward" at the Seaweed last night, or can give other information.

The police have little to go on. Two of the raiders were masked with balaclavas, one with a scarf. All were probably aged 25 to 30. One was blond, and another spoke with a Liverpudlian-type accent.

They smashed their way in through little George's bedroom window, after climbing on to a flat roof.

After the ordeal, Mrs. Bannister found her small son sitting crying in his glass-strewn bed. Fortunately the child had remained half-asleep throughout the nightmare incident.

# CHAPTER THREE
# THE KNEE CAPPING

That same night some Two Hundred and Fifty miles north in Liverpool, the nob was in the pub as usual with most of the boys apart from a few. The few were actually serving lots of years in the nick. In fact the nob had left one of them on a bungled robbery, he was said to have driven off and left one of his mates, that's mates for you eh!

Anyway, there was a lot of plotting going on around the table and a conclusion was made, they had been tipped off that the nob was going to be "had off", done in, beaten up on his way home. They weren't wrong either. Their plan was to send the nob across some waste land with a bright white bubble coat. If the attacker got him, the other twenty boy's from the firm would come out of hiding and get him. What a plan.

In fact they were so clever they even thought to surround the wasteland exits with their own men, then there could be no escape for the attacker. Magic, this was great. What a firm. In fact lets have more beer, this is going to be a victory so lets celebrate now. Word will be on the street tomorrow not to mess with them, as they had taught an attacker a severe lesson. They swilled more beer down, why not? They had something to celebrate.

Closing time was there again, it's like a swear word in Huyton. The nob came out the pub and looked around not to sure of himself, looking back to his friends hoping they would tell him to forget it, his hopes faded as he saw their thumbs all up in appraisal, after all it could turn out to be more fun than he expected. He was assured once again and off he walked.

The firm were all around so his confidence grew as he spotted the boy's all surrounding the outer part of the wasteland. They were at every exit on the field hiding, huddled into the shadows. This was a buzz. It was dark no moon, there was an eerie silence except for a car off in the distance on the other side of the wasteland, it was warm too warm for a coat, best keep it on though just in case the back up boys came to the defence and beat the wrong one up. Cannot be having that now, can we?

Half a mile from the wasteland, a car travelling within the speed limit and very cautiously carried three men wearing dark clothes. They pulled up just short of the wasteland and got out. They had pistols and a sawn off 12 bore shotgun under their jackets. One waited by the car with a pistol whilst the others walked to the wasteland.

They knew from a source at the pub exactly where,

and what was going on. As they walked to the entrance of the wasteland they noticed strange shadows and movements in several places. The stage was set, the audience were waiting for a performance, they were going to get one and they did not care.

They were glad they knew the fella they wanted was going to be dressed brightly sticking out like a fog lamp in the dark, he would not be very hard to miss. They stopped still waiting for the fella in the white coat to get within yards. The white coat stopped and they all confronted each other menacingly, then out came the shotgun.

It was pointed directly at the white coats head, the gunman knew exactly what he was going to do. The white coat seemed to expand as his face went the same colour as the coat. He lowered the shotgun and then decided to clip him, that is just to wing him and then his business would have been done and dusted.

White coat was definitely full of surprises and started doing the jig, he started dancing, must have been the lager eh! Well he carried on dancing and the gunman just pulled on that trigger gently, so gently it was to the gunman, the lovely feeling you get just as you cum. Then click, with an almighty BANG!!!

The Wasteland lit up like daylight for that split second. The bang was a drowning, echoing boom like a bomb. You would have heard it in Glasgow. The noise ripped through the night like thunder. The gunman did not hear the screams as his ears were still booming from the Shotgun bang, he walked back to the car and watched on as lots of people ran around in the shadows running for their lives in a panic.

Was this not the victory they were all celebrating in the pub just minutes before? I mean what's happened to the celebration drink? That's not fair, some fucker's have just jumped out with a sawn off shotgun and spoiled the party! We can't be having that now can we? Lets call on a meet again. Oh shit, did anyone call an ambulance?

There was a boost in sales for toilet rolls that evening and as for the people in the local area, they didn't get much sleep that night. There were ambulances with their screaming sirens, there were fire engines and almost every police car in Liverpool at the scene. It looked like an outside disco with the amount of flashing lights. Don't forget people were not shot every day in Liverpool in them days, it was a major event. A real life Knee Capping. It was a hit. This was to be a big event, especially for the police.

The case was assigned to Detective Inspector Tony Bennet. He was called to the scene immediately. He ordered for the Scenes Of Crime Unit to cordon off the wasteland, he ordered a round the clock guard at the hospital and told the police on duty at the hospital to keep him up to date with the progress. He had to be clever here as the locals did not talk to the police in general but he would recruit the local C.I.D's informer's and get the word from the street as to why and who was responsible.

The following morning he would talk with the press and organise a Hotline for any information and see where it would lead. He had the wasteland lit up with floodlights and the local police were searching the area bit by bit trying to find some clues. They were not successful and to make matters worse, the Scenes of Crimes officers could not find anything except pellets from the shot fired and blood. This was going to be a long night and he was not going to get any sleep by the look of things.

# KNEE-CAPPED!

## Man blasted in street ambush

SURGEONS were fighting today to save the right leg of a man ambushed by three gunmen just yards from his Huyton home.

█████████████, of Byron Close, was blasted with a shotgun at point-blank range after refusing to hand over cash.

**Full story: Page 2**

# 'Knee-cap' gun terror

**By Andy Byrne**

THREE GUNMEN brutally "knee-capped" a 28-year-old man as he walked home from a Huyton pub. And today, surgeons at Whiston Hospital were fighting to save the right leg of the man, who was ambushed on waste ground just yards from his home.

▓▓▓▓▓▓▓▓▓, of Byron Close, Huyton was blasted with a shotgun at point-blank range after refusing to hand over cash to the gunmen.

They ran off after the shooting — leaving the bloodstained victim to crawl 50 yards to reach nearby houses and raise the alarm.

▓▓▓▓▓▓▓▓ told witnesses he was walking home after drinking in the nearby Huyton Park pub when the men pounced.

Today, as detectives waited at his hospital bedside to get a detail statement, residents on the council estate near Huyton Quarry refused to answer questions about the shooting.

The curtains remained closed at ▓▓▓▓▓▓▓ ground-floor flat and milk lay uncollected on the step.

Det Insp Tony Bennett, of Huyton police station, said he had set up a 24-hour confidential hotline in the hope of receiving some information.

He said: "We are extremely anxious for anyone with information to contact us immediately, in the strictest confidence."

The hotline number is 777-2400.

# CHAPTER FOUR
## AFTERMATH OF A ROBBERY

The day after the Robbery in Southampton, all three victims were in hospital with a lot of police guards. Southampton had never seen anything like this before, heads would be rolling one way or another. It was heavily rumoured that the landlord was a resigned copper and was still a practising freemason. The landlord was pictured on the front page of the newspaper looking very battered and bruised.

The newspapers were having a wonderful day they had not had a story like this to write about for years. The T.V. were even going for it, radio too. This Robbery became so big that the police even made door-to-door inquiries to thousands of homes in the town. Had no one done a robbery in this city before? There were posters put up everywhere appealing for help and information. Even news bulletins on local T.V.

The police were getting hold of every snitch in every hole looking for clues. Every possible person was questioned but, the reality was there and the being, there was no one capable of doing such a brutal

Robbery that lived in the city. The detectives had nothing to go on. No one knew anything. A possible Liverpool accent was the only clue they had.

A week had passed in Southampton, nothing. The newspapers were still feasting on the Robbery and were still running the local papers with giant photos of the manager's face, they were looking for a tip off. It had an effect all right but not on the robbers, it was on the two C.I.D. leading the hunt. They were under so much pressure from every angle. The brewery's even got involved, they were determined that this could not happen to another one of their pubs. There were no stones uncovered this had to be solved, some ones head had to roll. The police were coming down hard. The pressure building up.

The landlord had only been at the pub for a month, he had come from the Ship Inn at Winchester. He had been the landlord there for a couple of years. He and his wife were a popular team, well liked by the locals. It had been a big decision for them to move on to the Seaweed pub.

The opportunity to make a go of it had been appealing. They could cook food and make the business work, turn it around into a sort of Harvester style restaurant. The Pub was set back in a small village-looking area called Woolston. It was across the water from Southampton City and to get there you had to cross a bridge.

They didn't know but to the locals the bridge was known as Suicide Bridge. It was the only way to get to Woolston if you did not want a thirty-minute drive. As the only other way to get to the mainland would be to drive all the way around the outskirts of the city and take the ring road in to the town. It was only now that the Landlord realised just how secluded the Pub was and how vulnerable they really were.

The area had a high population of travellers. There were a lot of them living there. The travellers had always had a good name and they were very respected. The area also had a few of its very own high-rise council flats, which were surrounded by thousands of houses on council estates. It was quite a rough area but the landlord did not know that.

All they were shown was, the nice little village and the nice little pub set back within the trees. It looked a great opportunity. They didn't know that there was also a rising drug problem on the estates. They were living in a nightmare, not a sleepy little village. How they regretted taking the Seaweed Public House.

What had they done wrong to deserve this? They were a hard working family striving to get somewhere in life. They had travelled the world and spent many a night in some dodgy looking places but never experienced anything like this. How could they have foreseen what was to happen.

The landlord Roger Bannister lay in his hospital

bed asleep with his wife Sarah, sat by his bedside holding tightly on to his hand. The nurses had injected him with strong painkillers to let him rest and feel no pain. She sat there weeping looking at the mess he was in, his eyes were swollen, his nose and jaw looked to be broken and his lips looked so thick they could burst any minute. She could feel his pain.

The police officers kept on coming in and assuring her that they would get the animals responsible. They promised her they would be outside the room and she could rest at ease. She could not rest though, not as she looked at her husband and the shock of the last evenings raid were just too hard to forget. She was still in shock. Could she get over it she wondered and she thought to herself that none of them could or would ever get over it, who could?

# CHAPTER FIVE
## BACKLASH AND HATRED FOR K DIVISION

Back in Liverpool the newspapers were having a good day, a gangland shooting, a real live hit. Boy this was good as there had been very few shootings in the town, they even knew who had done the shooting. The police had told the media not to expose the name until he was apprehended. They had a statement. In fact they had several statements, it seems that people could not wait to tell everyone they knew what they had witnessed. Even people that had dreamed of it wanted to say things, as it became a reality to them.

Where was the silence, where was the hard men of Huyton? They were writing statements and playing both sides of the fence, they were even getting picked up and arrested on the street corners, it was made to look like arrests, as a friend of the family from Plucky farm (another estate in Huyton) had heard over the scanner, he was shocked. So was I.

I was in Hull the next day seeing a friend of mine when I was passed a message. I went straight to the phone box and made a phone call. I was wanted by the police. That's nice eh. I wondered what that could be for? Well, I finished my business there in Hull and off I went down the motorway back to Liverpool. I had done nothing wrong so why shouldn't I?

As I came onto the estate in Huyton I saw little maggot on the corner, that was his nickname anyway. For some reason he ran the opposite way to me. I didn't take that much notice of him. I stopped at my flat where I lived to see my girlfriend but she was out.

I then went to my mother's home to have some tea. Sometime later in the evening I noticed out the window that there were people coming towards the house. Masks on their faces. Some had their hoods up and faces covered, I shouted for everyone to move away from the windows. The windows started to smash and the house was under siege by at least 30 gobshites.

They smashed at the windows and smashed the cars but no one entered the premises, lucky for them to say the least. Arms were coming through the windows but my mother walloped the shit out of them.

They backed off and run off into the night like little rats. That was a serious breach of crossing the line. I was not happy and neither was my family. A few minutes later there was lots of police outside the house carrying guns openly. I took leave through the back garden and was driven out of the way by a friend of mine.

The police were looking for me, they were not interested in asking about the house and car damage or if my family were ok. No! They wanted me Tony Allan, for attempted murder. Apparently several people had put my name forward for the shooting the night before. Well fuck them, they would have to find me first but not before I got some pay back for the damage these shits had done to my mother's home.

It was discussed between my family that a move back to Page Moss would be a good idea, It's basically just another estate not a stones throw away from this one. It's the one we all grew up in. Home. So the move was done and I was still "on the run" from the police.

They, the big bad gobshites, the men that run Huyton, persistently gave my mother and sister a hard time. They would pull up in cars and spit at them, threaten them, what they were going to do when they got me, the same old shit. They had promised my mother that I would next be seen in a body bag. Such brave words from such brave people.

One little prick called Tony Rogers made himself real busy. He did not tell his friends he was "arrested" and was telling the police everything he could. The rat knew he was on my most favourable list of people to visit. Rogers's close friend told every one that I had been to his flat banged on the door and demanded he should face me.

It transpired as rumour had it that he refused to

open the door so, I am alleged to have nailed it shut, pour petrol through the letterbox and set fire to it. Then beckoned him to jump out the window whilst I was supposed to be holding a meat cleaver, waiting for him.

How else do you get some one out of a place who was barricaded in? There were lots of stories that I had done this and I had done that. At the end of the day they came to my mothers house. That was the wrong thing to do, they could have gone to my flat, I was not hiding.

My girlfriends uncle was one of the main lads and swore he had nothing to do with any of it. That was crock, he was a nice man and I had a bit of respect for him. I also had a bit of respect for Barto, he was one of the hardest lads I knew from that area but not a liberty taker. He was with one of Tony Rogers' sister's, the girls in that family were all ok.

This other firm of gobshites had more than pissed me off, the police were now booting doors in and making life uncomfortable for any one around me. The heat was on. I was sick of my mother getting dragged into the police station, my little sister too and she was only about thirteen. The police were stopping all the family's cars and searching for guns and anything they could think of to harass them. I hated them.

My hatred for the police came from a young age, about eleven. The police burst into our family home in Page Moss one night, the "wrong address" the police said later. Bollocks to that one. My dad was in the

Dovecot pub one night and this big fella asked him outside for a punch up. He obliged and fought the fella, fair and square fist to fist.

The police came from everywhere all of a sudden and it transpired the big fella was a copper. It turned out that the copper was a fair man and shook hands with my dad, he warned the other coppers off and told them it had been a fair fight. The rest of the pub was behind my father and all watching the fight, the police licked their wounds and left the car park with their big fella.

A week or so later the police burst through the family front door and choked my dad till he was unconscious in front of my very eyes. My mother was dragged all around by her hair, one of my younger brother's Stephen who was only ten was belted to the floor. Frank my youngest brother who was only eight was thrown around, I got a crack on the head from a truncheon. They dragged my father off into the night, they had kidnapped my dad!

The next day he was physically held up in the dock at Huyton magistrates by three coppers, accused of assault on six coppers. The wounds to the police were a scratch to ones hand, a bruised elbow and several hand wounds. My mother did not recognise my dad, she was in shock. The bastards had re-arranged his face like the elephant man. He had had the hiding of all mothers, he was fucked and he could not even stand up on his own two feet. The police had battered him to a pulp.

He eventually got discharged from all the charges and being a non-criminal decided to sue the police. Very correct indeed because the week later the same coppers from K'Division grabbed another fella, a fifty odd year old working man called Jimmy Kelley, may god rest his soul. They kicked the shite out of him too. In fact they killed him, they beat him to death and did the coppers get convicted of his death? No they never, do they ever?

It took my dad five years to sue the police and even though it was a result, it was not good enough. He had endured five years of total harassment from the police, he got stopped in his car seven times in one night. Each time he got a search and told to produce all of his documents. So, now you know why, my hurt turned to hatred.

This looking back I would say changed my life, my whole families life. The system let us down, I could never be the same again. Neither could the members of my family. I swore after seeing the state of my father and what they had done to him, that anyone ever raised or put a finger on him again and I would deal with them severely. Was that such a bad thing?

I watched my father work all his life, he was not a thief or a robber and had never been to prison. He was a hard working man, he was a coalman. He was out at five in the morning and would return home in his lorry late each night and he would be black, covered in soot.

My father and his brothers were all working on

the coal together. They were a working class family like most of the people from Liverpool. They worked more than hard, even when they were ill. Workers have always deserved respect in my eyes no matter what their job. At least them people working for peanuts are working and earning a crust for their families. No one can take that away from them.

# CHAPTER SIX
## STAYING LOW ACROSS THE MERSEY

Time went by and I was staying across the water in Birkenhead with my girlfriend and a mate from down the coast, Billy Willis. He was a good sort and loved a drink. He had given his missus V.D. the week before and she was so impressed with it that, she sent him on holiday to stay up North with a bin bag full of shredded clothes. How nice. It was Christmas Eve and we were drinking in the local pub.

There were not many people in the pub but I knew most of the people that were there by face. I remember we had a lock in, an after hour's drink and by midnight I was whacked. I asked the manager was it ok for my friend to stay and drink some more, it was fine. I made my farewells and parted the pub with my girl.

We got back to the flat and two of the locals who I knew were at the flat. They were brothers. I went off to bed with my girl and thought to myself, what a lovely evening it had been. I woke and realised Billy was back, he was standing by the bedroom door saying what a fight he had put up. He had got a good hiding, he had blood coming from his ears, eyes and nose. All I heard from Billy was they had done him with bats in the pub.

That was it, I snapped out of my slumber They had beaten the fuck out of Billy, after taking the piss out of his Southampton accent. I knew I had to defend him and still full of lager, we all headed for the door except for my girl who I told to stay. Off we went to re-introduce our selves. The four of us went back to the pub in my car.

Billy had no weapon and the two brothers had sticks, I didn't want a weapon. As we got to the pub, I told everyone I was going to leave the keys in the ignition just in case something went wrong and one of them had to drive. It was made perfectly clear that no one was to leave without all four of us together.

The pub doors were locked and you could not see through the frosted windows so I knocked a few times. I could see movement through the frosted glass. They were taking the piss. I took a few steps back as the doors opened, I knew it was going to go off. I let two of what I made out to be around six men, get on to the pavement with their bats in hand. I just went for it and run in to them throwing punches at them.

They must have been in shock as I could hear shouts from the ones at the back telling the others to run for the cellar and that there were loads of us. The two that were out first were trying to retreat through the doors, they smashed the pub door right through. It was hanging on by the top hinge but it gave enough room for them to get in. I was first in after them and see the last one of them trying to get into the cellar. I caught him with a kick to the wrist and screamed some obscenities at the rest of them.

Some how they locked the door to the cellar. I then turned to the bar and told the girl behind the bar to run, she did. I picked up one of their bats that had been dropped on the floor and smashed a fruit machine, shouting more obscenities at the cellar. I had lost it a bit as I was feeling responsible for Billy's beating, I should never have left him alone in the pub.

I knew it was time to go. I grabbed Billy by the arm as he stood in the middle of the pub staring in to space and shouted to go, as the others must be in the car and we left sharpish. As we stepped outside onto the pavement the horror hit me. The car was gone, vanished. Marvellous eh! The two brothers had deserted us and gone. They must have gone when I entered the pub, god knows what would have happened if the fellas in the pub would have stood and fought. Shitbags had left us to it on our own.

That's when I heard the sirens, lots of them. Time to run. It was hopeless as the town was like a deserted ghost town at that time of the morning, we had to hide. I helped Billy get over a wall as he was still a bit fucked up. I got over another wall and hid behind an outside staircase. I heard the cars and vans Screeching to a stop on the other side of the wall, there was a lot of coppers at the scene. I could hear them all shouting and running around.

My stomach turned as I heard the gate open to the garden I was hiding in. That's when I heard a big commotion going on, a lot of swearing and the one thing I did not want to hear, Billy's protests, yes they had Billy. These two motherfucker brothers had took off in my car and left us, unforgivable. What I would do to them if I got away.

A torch beamed in my face, ok I was collared. There was nowhere to run, nowhere to hide, I was Donald Ducked, absolutely fucked. I put my hands out in a sheepish submission and then the crowd of coppers surrounded me.

When I say I was expecting to be cuffed, I mean "Hand cuffed". I see flash after flash, I was getting cuffed alright, as the truncheons beat viciously away to my face, head and body it was like a floating sensation. I must have fell unconscious a couple of times, as I could see visions in little bits but felt very numb.

One second I was on the floor at the back of the pub then I was by the gate getting dragged by the neck, then I remember staring at the floor trying to figure out where my legs had gone, it was all in sections. Slow motion. I remember they dragged my head upward and they were shouting to someone, asking them if I was one of the people. All I heard was the woman shouting that she couldn't tell, she was not sure. Obviously they were trying to do an I.D. on me to see if I was one of the people smashing up in the pub.

I thought they would have beaten me up later but these coppers were all fired up and enjoying their Christmas Eve. They stank of alcohol. Well it was not surprising that I was not positively identified, I didn't look like myself any more, I was now in disguise and looking more like a burst tomato. I am glad no innocent person was out walking their dog, or out getting some fresh air. They wouldn't be able to explain to these drunken copper's why they were out at that time of night, these copper's just wanted to give out the beatings and ask questions another time.

I was dragged to the back of the van, closest to the front of the pub, doors open and waiting, just for me. How nice, my chariot awaited. I was taken to the roadside and was stood up against the side of the van, I was thankful to lean back on to it, my body was now with me again. I must have still been a bit wobbly on my feet or looking unsteady because these two nice Bobbies were holding my shoulders up firmly against the van, one on either side to stop me toppling side ways. How considerate.

It was the bobby in front of my face that caught my attention most. He was built like a fucking mountain, he was definitely a rugby team, all in one body. He must have been cold as he was showing me in a slow elaborated way, how he put his gloves on, that was a good old demonstration just for my benefit.

By the look in his eye, I just knew he had taken a liking to me. Well, he was getting closer to my face now, I could smell the ale on his breath as well. He was smiling at me, yes he definitely liked me. He seemed excited about something.

Bang! Who turned that fucking light off? Hey, I was back again, the lights were dodgy around here, he stepped up again and I could not feel anything. All I knew was this copper was grinning from ear to ear trying to mouth words that I could not hear or understand, for some unexplainable reason the lights kept going out.

I remember lying face down in the back of the van on the floor, I asked Billy to pack the messing around in, so I could get my head together. I got no answer as he was fully occupied playing police van rugby, with his hands cuffed behind his back. I still to this day have not met a man who has won that game, I'd like to meet the man who does.

We eventually got the five hundred yards to the police station some thirty minutes later, I take it we two were not very good at their games and took the belting without too much of a struggle. If we had played I expect we would have arrived at the police station at least a few hours later. I think we were lucky as lots of people have been seriously hurt in the past.

I was now standing at the desk and Billy was standing several places away, although there was police in the middle and behind us, we still managed to keep our humour. The desk sergeant was very impressed with our good looks, he was not amused that Billy and myself had allegedly stood toe-to-toe with 24 coppers in a furious fist battle for forty-five minutes. I almost believed it myself as I heard the story. Just one thing puzzled me, why was not one copper suffering an injury, you know, like a scratch or a bruise?

Well that's Liverpool and that's the way it was. I got no complaints, no one ever listens anyway, it's an every day occurrence. I stood there thinking that I just wanted to go to a cell and sleep, but no, not tonight, it was Christmas and everyone was in the Xmas spirit. Everyone had had a skin full of ale.

We were asked our names and Billy obliged with "Charlie" yes, "Charlie Cornflakes." I responded with the first name that came into my head. "Peter" yes, wait for it, "Peter Weetabix." I somehow awoke in the cell trying to piece together the previous events. I could not remember too much since being asked my name at the charge desk.

I was in that cell for Seven days. Billy was in his own suite to. I would be sleeping and I would awake amidst flashes from the digs they thought I deserved time and time again through out the night. I was frightened to sleep, as every time I dozed off I would awake with coppers by my side, asking if I was alright. Every time they spotted me sleeping they would sneak in the cell and wallop me then ask if I was ok, as if they were concerned. I then refused to tell them my real name.

By the third day I knew that it was time to get a solicitor. My family would have known that I was in custody by now as Tracey would have told them. It was time, time to face the music. I later learned that Billy also waited a few days before giving his name in and asking for a solicitor. He also gave his Southampton address in.

The police in Southampton received a fax message that day, requiring all information about William Willis. They also made it clear to the Southampton police that Willis was in custody for an extremely violent offence concerning a public house, along with a very, very dangerous man from Liverpool.

I was sore as hell and very bruised. My right eye was open but only a little and there were bruises all over, thankfully no broken jaw, very sore but not broken. My nose I couldn't tell, it just didn't work and felt like a fat blob on my face. Boy was I sore. I gave them my real name and asked for a solicitor.

Within an hour after doing so, I must have had Forty different coppers come to the hatch in the door of the cell and stare at me, I could hear their whispers. I felt as though I were a peep show. They seemed shocked that I did not look like the photo they had of me. This was making me curious but I didn't let on, I had nothing to say to them, never have and never will. For some strange reason I did not get to see my solicitor till the next day. I was getting pissed off.

# CHAPTER SEVEN
## QUESTION TIME AND COURT

The cell door swung open and in the doorway stood several very well dressed men in suits. Very conservative looking with a menacing aura around them, as they stood and stared at me. Who the hell was this lot? They explained that they wanted to speak with me and that my solicitor was awaiting my presence at the interview room. I went along and sat at a table, no solicitor. There were four suits and myself in the room, my solicitor would be along shortly I was told.

They had dossiers on the table that caught my attention, I just made out my name and some letters, C11. It meant nothing to me at the time. The main suit sat and stared coldly at me not faltering at all, the others seemed edgy, it was creepy. The silence was broken some minutes later by the main suit. It was put to me that the solicitor did not need to be there at that moment and that it will be a formal interview when he arrived.

I said I had nothing to say, I didn't speak to strangers, my mum had always warned me. The main suit was tall, well-built and extra sharp, hair dark brown and finely cropped, perfect in stature. He could have been a Lord, he tapped his fingers patiently, he sported an onyx ring on his left little finger. He was definitely of extreme importance, he carried the air of menace, a ruthfulness not to be disobeyed. He made me feel uncomfortable and nervous.

The main suit just stared at me and one of the suits mentioned a name, Detective Chief Inspector Bennet. The main suit then got to the point. He was very straight and tried to intimidate me like a schoolmaster telling a naughty schoolboy off. He asked where I was on a particular night some months previously and I did not respond, why should I? I did not keep a diary, I just let him carry on and speak, I did not even think about where I was.

I was just patiently waiting to hear what he really wanted to say, it paid off. He was direct and asked me outright if I had shot a man from Huyton in the legs on some wasteland, on an estate called St. Johns in Huyton. I listened contently as he carried on and told me the man was Knee Capped with a shotgun. Then he said the man had made a statement in the hospital and named me as the shooter. He then went on to say several others had also witnessed the event and they had also written statements.

He mentioned a punch up in a pub and that I was beaten up and that's why I shot him. I replied after a long silence and told him I didn't even know the fella they named and I wouldn't know how to hold a gun or shoot one, neither I would never ever think of shooting someone. That was me done, I denied all knowledge of the people and the shooting.

The main suit was quiet and realising I was not going to elaborate, apart from my denial, carried on speaking. He then mentioned the fact that the shot victim had retracted his statement some time later and wanted to know if I knew why, had I got someone to put pressure on him? As before, I sat in silence with nothing to say.

The thing that struck me as unusual was the fact that if the man whom had been shot had of made a statement, why did he not show it to me? Surely if he had the accusation in black and white he would have used it and shown it, was it all a load of old cobbler's. Was my bluff getting called?

He carried on, he mentioned to me that I would not get away with it and that I would pay one way or another, I was going nowhere for a long time. I reiterated that I did not know anything and was taken back to my cell. I felt I had been intimidated and threatened, where the hell was my solicitor?

It was the fourth or fifth day that a solicitor turned up, so I was led to believe. It transpired that he had been in and out of the station since boxing day, he had been told I was not there by the police and they didn't know of any one arrested on Christmas eve. The solicitor Paul Rooney was not amused when he was allowed to see me.

He told me that if I had of given my name in, I would still not have seen him because in his mind they were hiding my beating. He was disgusted with my appearance and demanded that I was to be photographed, it just so happened that the police camera to take the mug shot was broken. Fancy that, well what did we expect?

Anyway, I was taken for another journey to the interview room and questioned about the incident at the pub on the Christmas Eve, I just said what I was advised to say by my solicitor and that was, "no comment" to everything. I mentioned that the coppers had beaten the shit out of me and I was the victim of police abuse. That fell on deaf ears.

Well, I was a victim was I not? I had been charged with; 1. Aggravated burglary. 2.Grevious Bodily Harm. 3. Demanding Money With Menaces. 4. Assaults x 8 On Police Officers and finally but not least 5. Criminal Damage. How did they work this lot out?

Well, I had seen similar tactics like this before, I knew this was going to be a carbon copy of how they persecuted my father. Well, it all started straight away, my solicitor came to see me again and told me that I had already been to court, without even his knowledge and that my non-appearance was due to my violent nature. I was finally put before a Magistrate in person, some Seven days after my arrest on Xmas day.

Billy was standing right there with me. My solicitor gestured that there would be a bail application at the end of the procedure, it was as if he had committed a crime himself. Within seconds the courtroom was bursting with uniforms. After the court went quiet the prosecution began his admission and outlined the story. A little weasel looking man with sharp features and black rimmed glasses, he also sported an onyx type ring on his left pinkie (little finger), this is how it went;

The case was that, "Tony Allan and his General Billy Willis" with some eight foot soldiers had attacked a public house in a military style manoeuvre. The army of thugs had welded guns, swords and pick axe handles. They destroyed the pub beyond repair and there were several casualties under police armed guard at the local hospital.

The reason Tony Allan launched his troops into this attack was because the landlord, had not paid his weekly charge for protection to Tony Allan's army of thugs. Yes this was a protection racket mafia style and they had caught the leader with one of his high-ranking generals at the scene. This was amazing, this story was so great it should have been on T.V.

Statements were there said the prosecution but, were so sensitive that they would not show them at this time for the protection of the witness's. I thought that was it, but he carried on. He went on to tell them that I was an ex grammar school boy and was very bright, I was anti-establishment and that he would not be surprised if an escape bid were to be made.

He then went on about Billy's glorious past and that he was so high in the category of violence, he was injected in the head six months previously by the police in Southampton with tranquilisers to control him and his violent temper. Well, this prosecution was so fictitious I couldn't stop laughing, then when he told the court how Tony Allan and Billy Willis stood and went blow for blow with dozens of police officers, it was beyond me.

He even told the court that it was so traumatic for the officers that Eight of them were actually off work, under the stress of that Xmas night's violence under police doctor's orders. That was it, I roared so much with laughter that my stomach felt like bursting, the story was out of this world. The last words to the court were that the large amount of police was there for the public's protection and the armed guards outside, were for the protection of all in the court.

This prosecution could spin them he should have worked for Jackanory. I leaned over to my solicitor and told him to write it all down word for word, this done and I could ask for the evidence. Then I could prove the lies as, it was impossible to be true. There was no bail just direct to jail. Did I expect any different? We were both remanded in custody to Risley Remand Centre (Grisley Risley) for one week.

All I felt I had done wrong was break a fruit machine and threaten a few people. They started it by bashing Billy up. The people from the pub knew what they had done. I had not done what they had said in court and was sure that the people from the pub would not have written such statements, this was all weird.

I even found myself thinking that maybe I did do something really bad but, I couldn't remember or work it out. Deep down I knew what it was all about and it was something I would have to learn to live with. I kept seeing the eyes of the suit from the first interview and hearing his chilling and menacing words, " you're going nowhere".

# CHAPTER EIGHT
## SOUTHAMPTON BIG BREAK


Unknown to me at the time back in Southampton, the police finally got a break months after the robbery. The day after Boxing Day a young girl was arrested over a fraud and was in custody in Southampton. Jackie Kelly (no connection to Liverpool at all). This girl seemed to be associated with some of the local criminals so a search of her home was made.

It was a flat in a high-rise block close to the Seaweed Public House. Nothing was found illegal but a new and unused balaclava was found in her flat. Well, she might put it on and scare herself in the mirror for kicks, you never know. The police searching the place had informed the C.I.D. They fell over themselves to get to see her whilst she was in the police cells.

It was recognised that the girl was still high as a kite on speed, maybe some thing else. The track marks on her arms shown that she was no first timer to a needle but, I could be wrong it could be a rash. I suppose the burnt and blackened squashed up tin foil carefully folded in her pocket was not what a heroin user chases the dragon with, probably a lucky trinket that's got some sentimental value to her eh?

Never mind, there was something and within an hour of seeing the C.I.D she had made a full confession to the Robbery of the Seaweed Public House, she was even given a charge sheet to keep her company. Job well done thought the two C.I.D, officers and off they went to show their inspector that they had solved the case.

Some one give them dogs a bone. They were going to be stars. Sherlock Holmes and Nipper Read would eat their hearts out. This is what being a detective was all about, getting your man, or woman in this case.

What was said in the inspector's office I don't know but I can speculate? A couple of hours later they had a new plan. They had a fax in their hands, they were smiling and feeling good, they knew they were on to something good. The fax was still wet with ink and they were already thinking of the commendations to come.

The door to the cell opened and the wreck huddled up in the corner was without doubt in a state, she was free to go. She was ill and psychologically wrecked, this could not be happening. After a long and tormenting thirty six hours she was released and was heading to the local dealer, she was desperate.

She got back to her flat and stared at the mess, it was disgusting. It was ransacked and every thing she ever had or owned was broken or had jam and coffee splattered over it. The police had certainly searched her place thoroughly.

She pulled a chair up the right way, sat down and broke. She didn't want this life, she had to stop the drugs. She cried, she cried till there were no more tears. She threw the small wrap of powder into the sink and turned on the tap. She had to stop somewhere along the line and now was the time.

It all started to come back to her, the deal was to point out the men in the photographs, say they were at her flat on the night of the robbery and because one of them was going to get life for shooting someone anyway, it didn't really matter.

The five hundred quid helped, few debts sorted, enough to piss off to her aunts in Biggleswade, Bedfordshire for a while, she had to get off the drugs. The photo's kept coming back into her head, the scouser Tony something...he seemed sort of nice. Tony Allan, that was his name and Billy Willis. Yes, she knew of Billy, who didn't in the town? He was a local. He was a nutter, there was so many stories of him being drunk and fighting. Brian Peters, that was the other Scouser's name she had to remember.

The C.I.D. had told her the one called Tony, was a killer and that he had killed a fella in Bournemouth, that he had Knee Capped several people and run protection rackets, basically everything was bad about him. For some reason his image kept penetrating into her mind from the photographs, it was making her feel uneasy, what if he found out? She knew she had to get her shit together and run, run far away. What had she done? Her conscience was running wild, how can she live with this? She couldn't help to put innocent people in prison that would not be right, she could not live with that. She eventually slept.

A week had passed since her release from the police station. She was getting into a state of total panic and paranoia each time she went out the door, she was under fire from every person that passed her, asking why she had done the Robbery and why was she involved? She tried to tell people that she knew nothing about it but they still treated her with contempt. The word on the street had come from the speculations due to the police raid and the inquiries made. They looked at her with disgust and hatred.

She went to see a close friend of hers called Ray Stanley. He was a skin head, wore the usual skin clothes of turned up jeans, Ben Sherman shirt, braces and shiny sixteen hole Air wear boots. Oh, and a well-shaved baldy shined head. To the general public his looks could be intimidating and one of a nasty looking lunatic. He was one of the main leaders of the Skinhead Organisation in Southampton and knew every one in the town. He also had a lot of respect in the criminal world. He was her friend.

She told him of all the happenings at the police

station and what had happened with the money they had given her. She needed help to sort this out, she didn't like the situation. Neither did Ray and he told her not to say anything to anyone until he found out exactly what was going on. He knew this was going to be trouble either way, she was a good friend in need of help and he felt he would have to at least try to help her.

He knew who Billy Willis was, he was from the other side of Southampton on the Mansbridge estate and Billy sported a wide reputation for being a bit of a nutter but not in the heavy league. He just hoped he could sort it with Billy. No one wants to be fitted up but this was real, so real that it was frightening. He advised Jackie to lay low for a while and that he would find Billy, they would take it from there. They said there farewells and off she went feeling a lot better and more in control of her destination.

A few days later she was at Rays door in a blind panic. She explained that one of the C.I.D. officers dealing with her called Detective Inspector Graham Essary had called in to see her. She explained that she was expected to be picked up at her flat in a few days and would be driven to Liverpool and placed in a hotel, so she can attend an Identification Parade and identify the named robber's in her statement.

She was in a terrible panic and Ray had to shout at her to calm her down. Ray thought for a while and come up with a solution, he knew from her that she had signed a statement written by Essary but, he also knew that if she now backed out she would suffer a reprisal from the police. As this was just totally unbelievable, he could only tell her to go on the I.D. parade and point out the wrong people, that way she may not be used in a trial later if it were to come to that. On the other hand she could just do a runner and go hide somewhere far away, until it all blew over and went away.

That would also give him time to get in touch with Billy and let him know that he was getting fitted up. This was shocking to Ray as he had only ever thought this shit happened on T.V. or in the movies. She left his place with two choices and only she could make them, what was she to do? She had but a few days to make her decision.

That evening as she arrived at her entrance to the block of flats where she lived, a familiar face appeared from the shadows. It was Essary the C.I.D. officer. He said hello in a quiet manner and asked if she was going to leave him out in the cold or, invite him in for a coffee and a little friendly chat. A bit of advice is what she needed he said.

She was shaking and feared she would be in trouble if she turned him away so, she said he could come in if he had to and have a coffee. She was not feeling well and was ready for an early night, he would have to be quick. He agreed that his little chat would not take too long and followed her into the lift.

The flat was on the sixteenth level and the lift took forever. She felt very uneasy and pulled her short skirt down as far as it would go, she could see Essary's eyes looking her up and down deliberately. She swore to herself she would never wear a short skirt again. Essary passed a comment on how long and beautiful her legs were.

She smiled politely and tried to avert the subject and told him she really did feel ill and could she not pop into see him at the police station another time. He told her it would only take a few minutes, she gulped and shook even more, she was very scared.

Once she got into the flat she said she would put the kettle on but Essary told her to go and get into bed, he would make it as she was not feeling very well. She tried an excuse but he insisted she should go and get into bed. She was terrified of him, she knew he could lock her away anytime he felt like, she felt she had no choice but to do what she was told.

She went into the bedroom and quickly searched for a pair of pyjamas and got changed. As she was changing she looked at the bedroom door, it was ajar. She knew she had closed it but she could see the figure of Essary looking through the gap. She chose to ignore it and pretend it was not happening. She went back into the living room and asked him what it was he wanted to see her about.

He insisted that she should lay down in bed, as she

looked a bit off colour. She went into the bedroom and layed down on the bed, covering herself with the quilt as he came in and pulled a chair to the side of her bed. He asked if she was still using drugs and she told him she had not used any since being locked up. He told her that he would like to check and see for himself and pulled away the quilt.

She shed a tear and in a feeble voice told him that she was clean. He ordered her to undress herself so he could be sure that his star witness was truthful to him and not telling him lies. She closed her eyes and undone her buttons. She wanted to die there and then she did not want to do this. She was trembling with fear but she knew she had to show she was on his side and do whatever she had to do to please him.

An hour later the front door to the flat closed behind Essary, she layed there on the bed curled in a ball naked, sobbing her heart out. Essary had told her before leaving that she owed her life to him and she would do well if she listened to him and done whatever had to be done. He had promised her a whole new life and a new name, as long as she followed through her side of the deal. He would also pop in to see that she was ok from time to time. He did on three further occasions.

# CHAPTER NINE
## REMANDED IN CUSTODY

It was the first week in January and I was looking forward to appearing at the courts. Risley had not exactly been a holiday but it was a week of sleep and recuperation from my beating at the hands of the police. On our arrival at the Remand centre in Warrington just outside Liverpool, we were processed like the other prisoners except that as we got out the sweat box (this is a big horse box vehicle, with steel cubicles very small, inside where the prisoners are sat and hand cuffed then locked into. No ventilation and very hot), we were singled out and taken to the side of the path.

I could hear an argument going on between the police and the warders. They were actually telling the police that they would refuse our entry into the centre, unless the police signed a disclaimer as to the damage showing on our faces. In other words they would only let us in the centre if the police agreed to a make a signed statement. One to state we were already marked and bruised when arriving at their centre. Hence, exonerates the prison service from any blame of the injuries we had sustained. I found it to be a sense of security in our favour, I was thinking that at last some one other than my solicitor could see a wrong doing and was doing something about it. Or so I thought.

As we went through the rigmarole of stripping, dressing, showering and endless documents to be signed, we were taken to a room where we were to be finger printed and photographed. We were held in what's known as the cage and mixed with the rest of the remand prisoner's who had arrived that day. All were finger printed and photographed in the usual way, except when Billy was processed the camera appeared to be broken. I knew somehow that the camera would fail for me, I was right, the camera had mysteriously broken again, how convenient.

I mentioned this to the others in the cage and they seemed genuinely amused, as they seemed to have expected it to happen. In the cage there were two big fellas whom sort of looked like typical bouncers. They kept on watching my every move, this made me curious very curious. I spoke to Billy and told him I did not feel right, he felt the same.

I made myself busy and asked one of them for a light, I was amazed that he called me Tony in his response. So, as not to be too hostile and wanting to know how they knew my first name, I struck up a conversation with them by asking them what they were locked up for. Apparently they were alleged to have let a shotgun off in a nightclub in a dispute over their wages and blasted the bar while it was empty. They had used a copper pipe, with an elastic band at one end with a nail inserted, this gives it a trigger effect by pulling it back and letting it go, it will hit the cartridge and fires out the other end. It is a homemade shotgun.

I in return answered their questions as to why we were locked up. They seemed to sigh with relief for some reason and laughed. I was curious and asked them why they were so happy. They went on to explain that they had been approached some days before on a visit by a friend of theirs, wanting to do a deal for them over their charges. There were two fellas in custody, who would be on their way to Risley, a Tony Allan and his co accused, they needed to be sorted and if they done the job they would get five grand and their charges dropped.

Well like most sensible people they done their own homework first to find out whom we were. They told me that each time they mentioned my name they were met with warnings about how dangerous I was supposed to be, they said it was common knowledge about the police enquiries into my so called criminal activities. They were shocked about the reputation building up around me as I was less than ten stone, gossip mongering had been full steam ahead and arms and legs were added to everything connected to me.

They were even happier to hear the real story and

about the charges we were facing to do with the pub. They had been told a different story completely and now believed it was more than a fit up. Some one out there wanted us hurt. I remember one of the lad's names to be Ducker's. He later turned out to be one of the main men from Birkenhead and a decent sort with his morals in order, I also met his brother Mark along the way.

Well we eventually got through the processing procedure of reception and we were put on the prison wing in different cells. I was put in with a little old fella, my first reaction was why the fuck are they putting him inside prison, it was not right. I offered him a fag and we got on ok. He too was from Huyton, the Western Avenue estate the other side of Jubilee Park where I had been brought up with my family.

His name was Jimmy Siega, he went on to tell me how the police had given him a rough time in Huyton Police Station, how they would not give him a drink of water not even a local solicitor. Basically, he was in for drinking on the street and telling a copper to fuck off, he was what I would describe as being like an old war dog, who had a few too many drinks and instead of taking him home and telling him off, they banged him up in the nick.

I promised I would let his brother Charlie know where he was if I was to get bail. I knew my family knew him but I had no hopes of bail in realism. So I tried to get a message passed on to his family for him, it was sad to see. He was harmless and there was just no justice in it, for anyone.

I was moved out of that cell and in with Billy and another lad called Barry Vaz. I didn't see old Jimmy again so I expect he was let out. Now, Barry was one of the lads and a decent sort, his story freaked the life out of me. Firstly, we should and would have met before hand but fate played a funny old part in us not meeting before.

A year or so before, I was in Bournemouth and a lad from Kirkby had pulled a crow bar out on me, so I went looking for him and punched him in. Little did I know was that this lad from Kirkby called Batty (Kevin Batt), had phoned up all his mates (Barry included) and told them I had beat him up while I was with a big gang of mates or something whilst he was on his own, with his girlfriend and kid. Well I suppose he had to save face somehow, as it was the opposite of what really happened. The lad was a prick, wanting all his mates to fight his battle with me.

Anyway Barry told me his story. He was on trial in two days and that was at the Crown Court in Liverpool. It was astonishing as he was only arrested five days previously. The average wait to get to the Crown Court was at least six months for a trial, or six weeks on a guilty plea. He was due to stand in the dock with Ian Smith for wounding with intent. Smithy was from the Bluebell estate and was known by half of Huyton as a very hard lad, he was and a good one to.

The accusations were that Smithy and Barry, had carved two brothers up with kitchen knives or something outside a chip shop in Baker's green, Bluebell. Well somehow within seven days Barry had to get all the evidence and read it, see where he needed to produce witness's etc and instruct a Barrister, then stand on trial. That was the power that the system seemed to have. I was shocked and in fairness to him he got what he deserved.

All four of us were sat together on the coach going to court some days later, I wished them the best of luck and they did me in return. They stood in the dock from what I later heard and were both found Not Guilty.

Their defence I heard, was that Smithy was in the chip shop and the two brothers had started on him and stabbed Smithy in the leg, he then took the knife out and proceeded to fight for his life giving the brother's hundreds of stitches to their faces. Self-defence and a Point of Law was the story of the day. I would keep that one in mind, as I may need to use this Point of Law at some stage for myself.

# CHAPTER TEN
## INTERVIEWED AND QUESTIONED

We were to carry on from the Liverpool Crown Court stop and continue our journey across the Mersey but not by Ferry. By tunnel to the Land of the Woolly Backs, that's what people are called outside of Liverpool. We went through the tunnel and were greeted by a large crowd of police in bulletproof jackets holding guns. There go the bail applications eh!

We both got signed into police custody and were taken to separate cells. I had took the precaution of mentioning to the prison guards that if I or Billy returned to the prison later that day looking like black and blue space cats they would be getting a summons to court, to prove we both left their prison in one piece. I was still sore from the previous beating and some of the marks were still visible on my face.

Within minutes of being in the cell I was told there was a visit from a solicitor for me and I accepted the visit. It was the solicitor's clerk and my stomache just turned, I needed a proper solicitor to deal with this lot. The clerk was only a couple of years older than myself,

I felt sick. They had sent me a puppy. Well, there was nothing I could do for now so I invited him to take a seat on the bench next to me. He held out his hand and more out of politeness I shook his hand. His name was Mark.

We sat and went through everything together and he kept writing and writing, he had even put the times down that he had been allowed into the station and the time he was allowed to access my cell. He had even brought a camera but, it was taken from him as he was searched. This fella was trying, I was getting to like him straight away, he was ok. I felt he believed in what I told him.

After an hour or so he went to find out what time the court would be set for and if they were still going to stick to the story portrayed the week before by the prosecution. Mark was back within ten minutes. He did not look happy. I was required for an interview with the C.I.D. from another region. They were from Southampton.

I asked Mark did he have any idea what it could be about, but all he knew was that it concerned a Robbery. Mark stated that if I knew nothing, just reply with a "no comment" to all of their questions, as he did not like the perculiararity of the way things were progressing at the station. I agreed to go on the interview to see what the hell I was being questioned for. I was no robber, I had nothing to lose so off we went.

I sat at the table and was introduced to the C.I.D. as Anthony Allan, they in turn introduced themselves in muffled voices and I only caught the one name, D.C. Graham Essary. He was about six foot, podgy build, black short curly hair and a round face with a moustache, he was around thirty-eight. The other one was around the same age but with mousy coloured longer hair and thinner in build. He had a thin face. Laurel and Hardy I thought.

After that they said their names again and sat down, there was no shake of hands or formalities it was straight into the questioning. They asked me where I was on a particular night some months previously, it was around the same date as the shooting I was questioned for. I was confused. I told them that I had "No comment". I then listened very carefully to what they had to say. I was told that whether I answered the questions or not, they were obliged to just continue and ask the questions.

I ignored the comment refusing to be engulfed in answering anything, as Mark said they would try to lead me into answering some questions then later on use it against me, saying that I was "selective", he said it was the way they worked. They continued and proceeded to fire their line of questions, it was Essary who fired all the questions at me. Was I in Southampton on the night in question? Did I commit a Robbery on a public house called the Seaweed? Did I know the pub? Did I know a girl called Jackie Kelly? Could I prove where I was on the night in question? Was I in custody at present for a similar robbery?

They tried a lot of tactics to get me to respond but, although I only knew Billy and of his girlfriend from that area, I had not even been to Southampton, I only knew Billy from Bournemouth. I knew nothing of these places or people. I refused to get involved with the continuous line of interrogation and kept to my response of "no comment".

My private life was my own, why should I be giving them a profile? My solicitor's advice was to be adhered to as he knew the system of law and not me. After ten minutes Essary said this was a pointless exercise and he was going to terminate the interview but, would I be willing to attend an Identification Parade? I nodded to Mark and he confirmed that I would be willing to attend any Identification Parade.

That was it, we left the room in silence and I was escorted back to the cell. Some twenty minutes later Mark was shown back into my cell again. What now I thought? Then he told me that I was required to attend an Identification Parade over in Liverpool, Stanley Road. This was to take place within the hour.

A special one way screen was set up so the witnesses could take part and it was all set up to happen. Mark did not want me to take part on the grounds that it was uncanny, strange, a little stink was in the air and he felt that we should have had more warning.

He had never heard of this type of procedure before. He was not convinced it was legal. I told him not to worry, as I had not done anything wrong so, if anything, it would stop them suspecting me. It would prove they had the wrong suspect. I told him that we should just get on with it, so he reluctantly gave them the go ahead.

I was rushed into an armed response vehicle hands cuffed behind my back and, my feet cuffed together at the ankles, with two giant coppers wearing bullet-proof jackets either side of me. I felt rather small and very intimidated. We travelled in a convoy of other police cars through the Mersey tunnel, having three response vehicles in front and the same behind. It made me feel as though I was a murderer. This was all wrong, what the hell was going on?

As I was travelling through the tunnel the copper's put a blanket over my head, I freaked out and went to kick off through instant reaction, only to feel a cold piece of steel on the back of my neck. This forced my reactions to stop abruptly. I froze and basically sat very still. I did not see if it was a gun, I was not told it was, I was not told it wasn't.

I was ordered to shut the fuck up and keep still. I had to do what I was told. The tension was very high and I did not want to be the main head lines on News At

Ten that night. "Bad man in custody gets shot in the head, trying to over power and escape from armed police in the Mersey Tunnel". I will be a good bitch sir! Three bags full sir!

I hated these Bastards so much and to think that what I was experiencing was real, I was up against the system, they would never admit to this behaviour, who would believe this carry on? Someone pinch me please, I must be sleeping. This was no dream it was a nightmare, a wide-awake one. I seemed to be the lucky bugger in the middle of it.

The blanket came off my head, I was in some forecourt and the cuffs came off my ankles. I was then walked into the station, led to a cell and the handcuffs were taken off. The cell door shut behind me, I sat down and tried to calm my nerves, I was shaking. It was not too long before Mark was entering the cell, he knew something was wrong. I probably looked the colour of a freshly starched white sheet. I told him what had happened in the tunnel, out came his pen again and he scribbled away.

He told me that he had called Paul Rooney and that he was on another matter out of town, so he could not get here to help. It was up to Mark to run the show. I chain smoked for at least an hour. Mark explained the procedure of how the Identification Parade would go. I listened carefully with interest. He explained there would be five witnesses, one after the other. They would walk up and down the screen and would pick someone out, or not be able to. I would be able to choose where to stand in the line up, out of the nine positions. I could also change my position before the witness entered the viewing aisle.

None of it mattered to me I just wanted to be out of this station as soon as possible. A Chief Superintendent came to the cell and explained that he would be conducting the I.D. Parade, if there were any queries he should be notified. Mark immediately asked to see where the witnesses were being held and where would they go after they had made their indications. Mark was led away with the Chief, in answer to his queries.

He returned some ten minutes later. There were to be two I.D. parades, one for me and one for Billy. He told me that one of the witnesses had not turned up yet, but the officers from Southampton had told the Chief that she maybe late. He explained to me that he was objecting to the manner in which the witnesses were to be put after the identification, he went on to tell me that they were all in one room and then one at a time they would be taken to the parade. He was clearly disgruntled.

After the identification the witness would be taken to a separate room but, to his anguish the room had a door in it that led into the next room, which of course was the first room. He told me the door had no lock on it and that it was wedged open because of their fears of an attack, as they were all so frightened. The Chief Inspector sheepishly stated that the witnesses have been told not to talk to each other until the parade was totally concluded.

My mind was doing acrobats, they could whisper to each other, they could give signs to each other, in fact they could probably comfort each other. Mark expressed his and my understandings of their ordeals but, neither of us would accept the room before and room after being adjacent, with an interior adjoining door wedged open. This was not agreeable by any means. That just was not fair in any respect. In fact it was well out of order.

The helpful Chief gave me an ultimatum, proceed or a confrontation will replace the parade. Mark explained that a confrontation was not what we wanted. He told me that I would sit in the cell and the witnesses would look through the hatch and say yes or no. This was a take it or leave it situation. I opted for the I.D. Parade advised by Mark.

Mark was writing everything down and asked the Chief to sign his note book as to verify what he had just stated, Mark was almost put in a cell of his own. The Chief went blue and accused Mark of interfering with the course of justice by questioning his integrity. Mark went a bright colour of crimson and told the chief that if he refused to sign it, he himself would become a witness to an unjust act of law.

He did stutter a bit but Mark stood his ground and I liked him even more. I couldn't help but giggle at the prospect of having Mark staying in jail with me. The Chief and Mark were at logger heads now and before I knew it, Mark burst out of his shell and threatened the Chief that if his client (me) was about to be fitted up his head would be first to roll. The silence was tremendous and the atmosphere electric, Mark had hit a raw nerve. What a clerk, I had the best in the land. I did not care now because I knew Mark was for real and was not about to be frightened off by anybody, not even by a Chief from Liverpool Police.

The silence lasted only seconds but seemed to last an hour, in that short space of time I visioned Mark getting done for five motoring offences and that was before he had took his foot of the break, I felt he was in as much trouble as me. This was all too much and I was getting paranoid, I could still feel the blanket over my head, this was all so wrong. The Chief seemed to check his temper and regain his clarity, he said we would have just on five minutes before the identification parade commenced.

It was at this point that Mark looked me in the eye and told me that he was bewildered, he believed that all the goings on were for ulterior motives not known by himself, he was worried and said it was becoming very farcical. I believed him. He told me that no matter what, he would be on the other side of the screen and taking notes of everything. That was all he could do in his power. I asked him how far it was between the witness room and the Parade room, he said around twenty metres. Something was now happening in my head and I didn't know what, maybe a sixth sense was kicking into action.

I didn't like this and I was nervous. It gave me a down feeling as though I were a lamb to the slaughter but, it also livened my brain right up. This was a serious predicament I was in, I had to be very, wide-awake.

They were actually going to go through with this Identification Parade and I knew that they knew, that I was not responsible. I was not a Robber I was a worker for god's sake.

# CHAPTER ELEVEN
## LIVERPOOL IDENTIFICATION PARADE

I entered the parade room to find eight people already in line, not one of them had short dark hair like myself but all were of similar age. I was asked if I would like to wear any of their jackets and I opted for one which was a plain blue zip up. I put it on and chose my position. Number two of nine, it was second from the end.

As the seconds slowly went by waiting for the first witness, I held the position. A deep sense of urgency came over me to move and instinct took over me, I quickly told number eight to swap. I shed the jacket and handed it to number eight, he slipped it on. It was done in seconds, just as they said the witness is about to enter the room. I stood trying to look relaxed, I was flustered, had someone turned the heating in the room up?

The ten seconds of deliberation passed in around two hours and a bucket full of sweat, or so it seemed. The first witness a man, said loud and clear that the Robber was "Number Two"!!! He was positive! I looked at Number two and would describe him as of stocky build, a round face with straggly hair down past his ears, a big sort of nose and brown eyes. Mark made a detailed note of the identified persons description.

My mind was ringing with alarms and the tension was unbearable, my heart was beating faster than a drum roll. The Bastards were trying to frame me here and I knew it, they were trying to put me in the picture. I heard the Chiefs voice loud and clear telling Mark that I must stay in the same position. Mark told him that I could juggle my position anytime I liked. It was under such and such an act, under the human rights comission, there was no putting Mark under the cosh, not now.

For the second line up I had to be shrewd. The possibilities were astronomical of what could happen next, or the way it could go, so I took my chances. This was more than a game now and it was my liberty in danger. I kept telling myself that I would be ok as I had done nothing wrong and the more I thought that, the more I didn't trust the surroundings.

I decided to play it the same way, so I chose to stay at number eight of nine, second from the end. They sent for the next witness a woman. I gave it a few seconds then told Number Two to swap again and we done the same as before. I could swear that they followed me around with a hot radiator, I was very hot and sweating freely, drips pouring down my back, the fear was rushing through me and my whole body was pumping. I felt I would stand out as I struggled to contain the rush of panic.

The witness took only five seconds and indicated as loud as the previous witness that it was "Number Eight"!!! That was the robber! Without any doubt! Another positive I.D. on the same bloke. I was not feeling to good now I was surely having a panic attack, I needed deep breaths to contain myself.

The reality was not real it couldn't be, the same place I stood in and swapped with was twice indicated, the lad looked nothing like me. I told them I needed a minute to collect myself and hold myself together, this just cannot be real. I didn't know who the witness's were, what they looked like or anything about them, it could be anyone for all I knew. I was thinking that if I do the swap again it would happen again, the same lad the same position of second from the end, who knew? It could not happen again surely.

I wiped my face on my sleeve it was very, very hot. I nodded that I was ready and stayed in the same position, Number Two. I waited again for a few seconds and told Number Eight to swap again, he was looking a bit nervous himself, I could see it in his eyes, he seemed reluctant all of a sudden, I stared at him and told him to be quick. Thankfully he did it in time.

I was now in position Eight and the other lad in position Number Two, both second from the end. The first two line-ups were on instinct, but now I could determine a pattern. The third witness entered the aisle and the atmosphere was electric, I felt myself shaking, I was trying to relax my breathing, I was sure I was going to choke, I needed to swallow but I dare not in case I did choke. I held on as the witness, another male stated that "Number Two"!!! Was without doubt the Robber!! The witness was positive!

I expected it, I knew it, it was now becoming more than obvious to me that who ever was relaying the witness to the room was letting something on, or the witnesses were telling each other something. More than strange that this volunteer had been picked out three times positively. It crossed my mind that for three witnesses to identify a person on a line up cannot be an accident, or is it a freak coincidence?

My body was relaxing now, as I knew there were two to go. I was going to play the law of averages and stick to the method that had transpired through my instinct, yes I could vision this in a mathematical way. It was a numerical system in force and very easy to depict by drawing a diagram on a piece of paper.

I stated that I was going to stay in the same position once again. I did not feel right. The probability of the second from the end to be pointed out for a fourth time in a mathematical expression be, odds on. I pulled the same move again and swapped position with Number Two just like I had done earlier. I waited as they stated the witness was about to enter the room and braced myself, my nerves were gone.

The witness took longer than the others and I began to panic again. I heard a woman's voice say "Number Two"!!! I felt explosions going off in my head, I just knew it would be second from the end and it was, but this time it was to be my number. I heard Mark quickly break the silence and ask if he could ask a question, he did anyway.

He asked the woman which one of the Robber's had she pointed out. She told him that Number Two was the Robber who was the ringleader. Mark quickly asked her what was he wearing on the night of the Robbery to which she replied, a full-face balaclava. Mark went in for the kill and asked her how did she recognise Number Two if he wore a full-face balaclava? Good point Mark, I was impressed. She stated quite clearly in the presence of the Chief that it was the, "Evil and Sadistic Eyes" of Number Two that she had remembered. She would never forget them for as long as she lived.

Mark then asked if he could have all the people on the Identification parade lined up wearing full face balaclava's to see if she could still point me out. This was refused. I did not know what to think. Number Eight was now asking for a break and said he needed some fresh air. To my surprise that was it, all over. The fifth witness who ever it was, had not turned up.

I was taken back to a cell and Mark arrived simultaneously. He was smiling, he sat down with me and my instant reaction was to ask him what it all meant. Well, first of all he let out a big sigh and shook his head. Mark then sat down and told me that he had never dreamt in his life, that he would witness and experience such a corrupt procedure. He was appalled.

The outcome in his eyes was very good for me. He explained that although the witnesses had all picked out the second from the end, by them picking out a local collage boy three times and being positive, it meant that there was more evidence against the collage boy.

He told me that my eyes were not Evil or Sadistic, he commented that they were like Paul Newman's eyes. He said anyone wearing a balaclava would have "Evil Eyes", as far as a member of the public would be concerned. A person in a balaclava would not be nice to see full stop and that anyone wearing a balaclava he stressed, could not be identified.

He told me that if I had not have moved I would have been in some serious trouble, so bad that he did not want to contemplate it, neither did I. Mark assured me that the I.D. against myself was totally ridiculous, he said you cannot I.D. someone wearing a balaclava or the S.A.S. would not wear them, plus the fact that three others had picked out another person, the same person in the same line up.

To Mark, aside from the entire dodgy goings on, he thought that it was proof that it was not me. He said it could never stand up for anything. I felt relieved now, I felt safe. Mark joked that if I ever heard anything from the Southampton Police again it probably would be an apology. I asked him who the witnesses were and why should I be getting the hassle, I didn't even know Southampton.

He told me that the only information he had about the witnesses, was that they were from the Robbery in Southampton and were the victims. They had all been brought up the motorway to Liverpool, to be here for this I.D. Parade.

He mentioned that because my co-accused Willis was from Southampton, that was probably why the police had done it, just routine. In fact Billy was going through the I.D. parade at this very moment, said Mark. I hoped it would be ok for Billy, he had not done the Robbery, besides he was not a thief he was more of a beer monster. We had already chosen a name for him and nicknamed him "Buffalo Bill".

Mark said he was going to check what time I was due to be returning to Birkenhead Court. He had to get over there to represent me in court. He would keep me up-dated on all the days' events. As he left he winked and said to me that now they know I am not such a bad egg, they might drop the Xmas eve allegations down to the true charge of Criminal Damage.

After all I had told Mark of the incident on Xmas eve, he had told me that he believed the charges from that night were "holding charges", so the police could hold me while they investigated the other accusations.

He said I should be looking at criminal damage to a fruit machine and after the good hiding I got, should be looking at a probation order if I made it clear that I would not sue the police for their behaviour that night.

It was tit for tat and seemed pretty reasonable to me. Paul Rooney had already filed complaints about the police's conduct and raised questions about the injuries that I had received.

I looked around the empty cell and felt as though there was a bit of justice somewhere in this life. I did not feel the same somehow, it was an experience I would never like to go through again. I had no trust in the system at all, that was gone. They had just tried to frame me, was I a lucky chap indeed. The door opened, I was hand cuffed and told I was returning to the courts over the water in Birkenhead.

# CHAPTER TWELVE
# MENTAL TORMENT WHILST
# ON REMAND

I was not ankle cuffed nor covered with a blanket on the way back, it was a five-minute ride and I was back in Birkenhead to face the local magistrates. I could feel the pressure lifting and I was feeling a bit better. I was beginning to feel a bit of hope creeping in. Come on Mark you can do it lad. I was praying that Mark was correct in his outlook. He should be, he had been around for a few years and I was beginning to realise why Paul Rooney had sent him to cover for him, he was good.

Mark had won me over on a big scale. I was looking forward to seeing him, I was now getting a bit excited with the thoughts of bail. They had to drop the stupid holding charges surely and the allegations of attacking the police were just pathetic, every one there could see that, maybe bail, maybe.

It was almost three hours before Mark was shown into my cell. The first thing he told me was that Billy, had not been picked out by any of the four witnesses and that was probably the last we would ever hear of it.

May as well forget all about it. Secondly, no luck with negotiating a tit for tat deal with the prosecution, plus the committal papers (that's all the witnesses statements), were not to be served for another week.

This was a blow as I needed to see the so called statements, it was the only proof I could get to show it was total fiction from the prosecution. The witnesses would prove I was not a lunatic on a destruction mission with an army of head cases. The way the prosecution had put it across to the magistrates had even scared me. I was pretty sure that the Hulk didn't pop out of me when I had a few too many lagers.

I told Mark that I would still like to apply for bail. He had spoken with my mother outside the courts and she had assured him of surety's (a surety is someone that will vouch for your return to court with a large amount of cash as a pledge, if you don't turn up at court you loose your money or your surety's money, ten thousand pounds he thought was quite enough). The application was refused, the effort was futile.

The magistrate did not even consider it for two seconds, the police had jammed into the courts once again and their presence was as over powering as the first appearance. There was no escaping this mass presence of intimidating policemen. So, off I went with Billy in the sweatbox, back to Grisley Risley.

It was almost six months before the trial. We were not given bail at any time. We met quite a lot of people who stayed there over that period of time and heard a lot of stories from other people's experiences. I was getting educated in the conduct of the system of law, procedures at courts, prison life procedure, basically I was absorbing all I could. I had to I had a fight on my hands. The time in the remand centre passed slowly almost every day the same as the one before. I shared a cell with Billy and got to know him very well.

I was visited quite often and Billy shared the visits, mostly from my two younger brothers, my mother and little sister. They felt sorry for Billy and the situation we were both in. Billy had not seen his wife since the week before Christmas, nor his two sons and they meant the world to him. All he had were a couple of letters and a photograph of his kids. He had been married very young. He was old fashioned and had took the hand in marriage of the childhood sweetheart he had put in the family way. He was not too popular with her family.

It would break my heart to see my mum and sister, as they were having a bad time still. They would never tell me what they were going through but other people did. The gang of idiots from the St. Johns estate had been harassing them. This gang was really doing my head in, they had tried to create a witch-hunt against my family. They really made me feel sick, especially a few certain individuals.

They had tried to drag my mother into a car, they

had told her what they were going to do to her, they threw things in the street at her and spat at her and my little sister and they didn't stop. The gutless bastards. My family did not run to the police and report them for what they were doing, not likely, my family did not believe in that, none of us trusted the police. These pricks would get it back. I would make them suffer more than enough.

This was not my family's dispute it was mine. These people were ok to bully and brandish women and kids but, when it goes back to them receiving a bit of trouble, they run to the police. Why couldn't they wait, I would not be away for much longer I hoped? They were not my type of people and I was not going to let things go, I would settle the score with them, give it right back, I was not a woman or child. Or is that what they was afraid of. I would give them a fight all right.

They would not do it if I was outside but, they knew I was locked in. It hurt every time I thought of it. They were cowards. I was helpless to protect my loved ones and this proved the mentality of them by having a go at women and children. They were low, they were gutter rats. One of the lads that stayed a while in the remand centre was from their estate and would tell me things that I ought to know. He told me that after my mother's windows and all our cars were smashed up, six of the attacker's were arrested.

The ones that were arrested were never charged,

why should they? My family made no allegations. A cockney family picked some of them up, and they went off to hide in London. I was very interested in this and after some weeks he filled me in on all the names and people involved.

I did not know any of the people in London, I just had names and the main one was "Ollie McCann". I would not forget that name in a hurry. Ollie was from a big family in Harrow. There was a car sent up from London to Liverpool to pick them up, I was told two of the gang travelled to London in the boot of the car, to frightened to stay in Liverpool, they must have done something very wrong to leave that way. Cowards.

My sleep was not to good, as I would beat myself up mentally worrying about my family every night. They didn't deserve to be humiliated by these horrible reptiles, the fury would rise through my body every time I thought about it. How dare they. Being locked up meant I was helpless. There was nothing I could do.

Although I knew that certain members of my family were not about to take any shit off them whether I be there or not, it did not change my feelings or make me feel any better. I learned to contain my emotions and sought sanctuary in the gym almost every day, I would burn myself out regular. Healthy body, healthy mind.

# CHAPTER THIRTEEN
## LIVERPOOL CROWN COURTS

The trial was set to start on a Monday and expected to last a week. We were set to stand trial at Liverpool Crown Court. There would be a Judge and a Jury of twelve men and women. The prosecution was a barrister with a strange coloured wig on, my barrister was the defence and Billy had a different barrister. Before they swear the Jury in, there was to be an argument on the basis of, points of law.

The defence barristers argued about certain aspects of law in relation to the charges separately and asked for all the charges to be thrown out on the grounds of insufficient evidence. They mentioned points of law and other jargon only known and understood by the law society. I just sat alongside Billy looking as if I understood everything but I really did not have a clue. The Judge was sat there nodding and agreeing with their points then asked or should I say, invited the prosecution to justify the charges and state the grounds for each charge.

This went on all morning, until the Judge decided

he would retire for lunch and give his findings in the afternoon session. Court rise. We were, that is Billy and I, taken down the hatch behind us in the dock and to the great big cell that was three flights of concrete stairs below. We were not alone in that cell, they was holding another man in there that was also there for a big trial. A Murder Trial.

He was called Arabekie, he was to stand trial for killing a young boy in Wallasey. The kid was chased by Arabekie and met his death a few minutes later, on a train line. I did not ask for the story or details and I never knew his first name, I dare not ask him, I did not even want to look at him. His head was lowered and it looked like he was doing some serious reading into a book and was not to be disturbed.

He was around six foot four, medium build and he was as black as the Ace of Spades. He was around Twenty-Five. His nickname was Purple Ackie. No one had ever cared to tell him that though, this fella was the ogre, he was the scariest person you could know, his reputation was astonishing, everybody knew of him, he was the one inmate at the remand centre everyone feared to have as a cell mate.

The stories that people had told me were beyond belief, every one of them more dangerous than the one before. Every body had a story to tell about him, he was the child catcher, the child killer, the one who loved young boys and I don't mean to play tiddly winks with.

He was a person who done what he felt like. Purple Ackie was the king of your worse nightmares, he was the one to fight so violently that even the prison warders would not go near him through fear, the stories were endless.

I sort of stopped in my tracks as I entered the giant cell, I looked at Billy and he quickly whispered that there was two of us, this didn't give me much encouragement. This fella was bigger than his reputation, he was massive. I walked to the opposite side of the cell and sat across from him, I couldn't get far enough away as there was nowhere else to go. I was in the shit now, I was sure the warders had put him here on purpose.

Billy sat next to me, we did not speak, we did not want to speak, a very long two minutes passed by. We knew this was a situation, a serious one. I tried not to stare at purple Ackie, I didn't want him to ask me what I was looking at then die horribly, I also didn't want to take my eyes of him. I didn't know what to do, I was scared to think in case he could hear my thoughts. I was trapped in a giant cell with the Bogie Man.

I tried to ask Billy if he wanted a smoke but I sort of got stuck on the first word and no words came out. This was not funny, I tried again and as I did Billy tried to say something, we turned to look at each other and both burst out laughing.

The silence was broken, we giggled our heads off

until Purple Ackie joined in the laughing with us. His laugh was deep and sinister sounding and really loud. We went quiet but he carried on, this made us more than just a little bit weary, he was a psycho, he must be, he's laughing about nothing. I hoped he was not about to go nuts, I prayed to dear god that he wouldn't think we had been laughing at him.

He stopped suddenly, then lowered his head and carried on reading. I was hoping that Billy did not want to go to the toilet, I did not want to be on my own, this was spooky. A minute went by and we began to talk about our case, what we had made of it so far, well what we could understand about it anyway.

We still kept our eyes on Purple Ackie, just in case he sneaked up on us. We were asking each other about what these points of law were and what all the jargon could mean when a voice came from the other side of the cell, I pretended that I did not hear the voice so did Billy. The voice sounded again and this time it came with a menacing authority, which had to be acknowledged. It was Purple Ackie, he was telling us he knew what it meant.

Somehow it seemed he might not want to try and kill us, he was trying to tell us in an understandable way what was going on in our court case. He could understand the court jargon and was like an encyclopedia of criminology to the Judiciary. This raving psychopath was a genius. We told him about a few things and he had all the answers, I asked him what C.I.I was and he told us it was not C.I.I. But, was in fact "C. Eleven".

This he explained, was a special department dedicated to observations and gathering collators based at New Scotland Yard, assigned to the home office. He went on to tell us how John Stalker, the high commissioner of the police force in the North West had upset him and how he had staged a protest outside the commissioner's home! Purple Ackie was terrorising a big time Police Commissioner. He definitely was a raving nutter.

I didn't really have a clue what it all meant but it sounded good and he was enjoying the tutorial. I just prayed he was not giving us this free lesson with the thoughts of us repaying him in kind! He would be in for a shock. I would die fighting him if I had to, he was not going to be having a squeeze on my muscles that was for sure!

We were called for court, thank god for that, we said bye and left with our backs very close to the wall. We climbed the stairs again and entered the court and sat down. The court was already sitting, they were waiting on us. There was a brief statement made by the Judge that I could not grasp, the jargon these people with wigs on were saying, was beyond my knowledge and understanding.

All legal points from Nineteen Fifty Three, Regina

versus Walker, paragraph seven.... or whatever they were going on about. I could hear the words but, the meanings were not clear in the context they talked. It was another language only for the judicial workers training or with a degree in law, the terminology of it was difficult to grasp for a normal person not living in those worlds.

The Judge then asked the prosecution if he was running along the line of a Protection Racket. The response was that they were going along that line. The Judge asked him on what grounds as there was not a statement in sight to suggest it could be possible. The prosecution replied that because of the violence used against the police and the military style attack of the pub, it would prove it was indeed for the motive of demanding monies.

I listened with intent and prayed the Judge would see the truth of the Christmas Eve events. There was silence for a few seconds as the prosecution sat down, the Judge then said his piece. The Judge told the court that due to not a scrap of evidence to indicate in any way, the remotest possibility of such an act in crime of, Demanding Money with Menaces, he would dismiss the charge with ferocity.

He then went on to state that he found it insulting beyond belief that he was to be expected to believe a nine stone boy and, a ten stone boy of such young ages could be trying to run a protection racket. He then threw out the charge of aggravated burglary stating that there was neither a mention of theft nor an allegation of Burglary.

Then he said sarcastically to the prosecution, did the prosecution want the Jury to hear that the two defendants had stood toe to toe with dozens of police officers, for half an hour having a punch up with their bare hands? If they did, then they the prosecution were in the wrong courts. He would not accept it. Out went the assaults.

We were both left with Criminal Damage. We were told to stand up and the Judge asked for our pleas to the lesser charge of Criminal Damage. I pleaded guilty to the charge. So did Billy. We had spent just on six months on remand, we was walking out here, we had to, we had spent more than enough time inside for such a minor offence, it was going to be over at last.

We were told to sit down and the defence barristers were asked to make representations on our behalf. The first to take the lead was my barrister, he went on to state that I had been punished enough for a minor crime and that the beating I had received, was a measure as in to the attitude and depth of the police's ferociousness in my direction.

The penalty should be sigh and die (this means that I had served a lengthy sentence already and it should be evened out as in sigh and die.), no more punishment, the defendant had, had enough he told the Judge. He was right, I had, had enough.

Billy's barrister said the same more or less, he mentioned that Billy was not even accused of breaking a fruit machine, he was a long way from home, his wife and children had not seen him since the week before his arrest and he had also suffered. This was looking good. We were on our way out the door here, at last I thought.

Then I heard a commotion at the door of the court, I turned, looked and stared. Several people were entering the courtroom, one wore a suit, I caught his eyes. It was the suit that looked familiar, I could not pin point his face. Several other suits and a uniformed policeman with a flat peaked cap accompanied him. It was the Chief of Police, Sir Kenneth Oxford, I was sure I had seen him on T.V. lots of times. They made a gesture towards the Judge and he called the hearing to a standstill, stating the court will now recess for fifteen minutes.

I thought to myself that what ever they wanted to see the judge for must have been very important, I didn't suspect that it could have anything to do with me, not possible, I was going home. There were some big cases going on in the building and a murder trial. It had to be something to do with them or something else, not me.

We were taken down to the holding cell again. No Arabekie, thank god for that. The two of us were excited, we got the impression we were to be released that day, very soon. Both our barristers had agreed that we had served more than the punishment for the crime. We were time served as the warders had said. Time went by and it was an hour and a half later, before we were called back up to the courtroom.

# Purple Akie 'put fear into boy who died'

TRAGIC teenager Gary Kelly turned pale with fear when he saw the man nicknamed Purple Akie on the day he died, Birkenhead magistrates heard

Akinwale Arobieke was waiting outside New Brighton baths when 16-year-old Gary came out with his friends.

His friends left, some climbing over a wall, and schoolboy Gary walked off looking behind him, the court heard.

A few hours later he was dead – electrocuted under a train at New Brighton station, allegedly trying to escape from Arobieke.

A statement read to the court from one of Gary's friends, Joseph Jason Berry, said Gary was terrified when he saw Arobieke and turned white.

## Campaign

Arobieke had allegedly threatened Gary, of Water Street, Birkenhead, because he said he had called him names.

Arobieke, 25, of South Hill Road, Dingle, is charged with Gary's manslaughter and 27 other

By Peter Sherlock

charges, including indecent assault and assault.

The committal hearing was told that Arobieke waged a campaign of terror against young boys and men, and felt their arm, chest and thigh muscles.

Some witnesses wrote their addresses down rather than give them in open court.

Colette Joyce said Arobieke was walking up and down the platform very slowly as if he was looking for someone.

## Scared

"He looked as if he was very alert. His eyes were very big as if he was looking around."

She said young men went very pale and appeared to be scared when they saw Arobieke.

Another witness, Terry Boswell, said: "I saw the coloured man looking into the train suspiciously. He was looking through all the windows. He looked like he was looking for someone."

He denied a claim by the defending solicitor, Julian Linskill, that he could not see properly because the platform was so packed.

Sean Johansen said in a statement that he was twice punched in the face by Arobieke, who said: "If I ever see you again I will do you in, so run."

He said Gary Kelly was terrified and had said he had to "keep low" to keep out of Arobieke's way.

Reporting restrictions were lifted at an earlier hearing.

(Proceeding).

# CHAPTER FOURTEEN
## SENTENCE FOR BREAKING
## A FRUIT MACHINE

Here we go, the butterflies were soaring around my stomache. I was nervous and filled with tension as we went up the stairs once again. We walked into the court, the Judge was not in his chair yet. I looked around and my mother was there smiling showing me her fingers were crossed, she mouthed that we would be ok, the barristers had assured her. My brothers sat looking around. It was not one of those places you go and enjoy yourself, they are horrible places. Not somewhere to go unless you have to.

Court rise. The whole court stood and let the judge sit down, that was the procedure and we commoners must rise in his presence. I was told to stand first, he went on to say that although he did not agree with the allegations to start, he still believed I was wrong to take the law into my own hands and damage others property. I agreed I was wrong and yes I should not have done what I did.

He then mentioned that he was of mind to release

me but, other powers had changed his judgement. I frowned, what the hell was he going on about. He then said I will go to prison for the maximum sentence for that type of offence, he could not send me there for longer, he paused briefly, I gulped hard as he spoke "Eighteen months"!

Then the judge told the warders to take me down. I was more or less frog marched down the stairwell. I was shocked. The warders had hold of my arms and I braved a placid look and nodded to my mother as if to tell her not to worry. I was sickened, I was devastated. This sentence could not be right, no one gets eighteen months for criminal damage, it was outrageous.

Billy soon followed me. He did not walk out either, he was handed a twelve-month sentence, for what? That poor git had not even broken a fruit machine or even shouted, come to think of it he had not said a word, just took a battering. What the hell was going on? Our barristers soon came down to see us in separate interview rooms.

My barrister told me that the Judge did not want to send us back to the prison but the judge was influenced from unseen quarters. I asked him if he could clarify that in plain English. He went on to tell me that whatever the interruption was in the court when the Chief of Police turned up, it was to discuss a serious nature concerning me. They had held council with the judge and discussed the risk of me being released back on to the street.

I could not believe it, I told him I had done nothing, I was just a normal person not a big time gangster. He shook his head and spoke quietly almost whispering and stated that, according to the senior police officers in Liverpool, I was a threat to the City and was highly dangerous. He had heard it himself but was under the official secrets act and could not elaborate or verify what he was telling me. I was more than in shock, I was now in total confusion.

He told me he was so sorry but there was nothing he could do as an appeal would be futile. He told me he knew the Judge quite well and earlier the Judge had indicated that he would be releasing me. He said he was a very fair Judge but, the highest-ranking police in Liverpool do not turn up at the last hour for nothing. Something I had done was so bad, that it had made it necessary for them to approach the Judge like that.

I asked if this was legal and he told me that he would not ever be able to prove that this type of action has taken place. I was taken back to the big cell once again, I had to hold my head up and get on with it. I would have to serve two thirds of the sentence which would be another Six months. Twelve months of prison I would have to serve all together.

Billy had just on two months left to serve, he had been sentenced to Twelve months and had to serve a total of Eight months. I told him to think of the two months as a "getting ready" period for release. I soon got my head around the extra six months and kidded myself that it would soon pass. I had to keep my spirits up and soon our moods changed completely, one of the warder's came in and told us that our friend would not be joining us again.

Arabekie had been found Not Guilty! He was up for Murder and he was now walking the streets. This was all too much. Why lock someone up for murder and let him walk out, I was not wise to this law profession. I was relieved though, Purple Ackie would not be locked up in the big cell with us.

Bye went the time and six o'clock came. The cell was quite full of people who had been sent to prison that day, all the courts had closed and we were all ready to go. There were a variety of people in the cell, one of them was called Rutherford. His brother was in a famous pop group, "Frankie Goes To Hollywood". He was on trial and was only part heard, so he was to spend the next day there.

Another fella, a big fat one told us he had got four years for handling stolen goods, it was a block of cheese he said. We must have been so naïve to believe him, as it turned out he had got the Four years for a sex offence. One of the warder's asked us why we had not taken our frustrations out on him. He was apparently put in with us for our pleasure.

# CHAPTER FIFTEEN
## SURPRISE VISITOR AT WALTON PRISON

We eventually got to Walton Prison. We had to go through the whole reception process once again and wear the prison issue ill fitting uniform. A lot of inmates were doing long sentences and some of them had been given Eight years and upwards for armed robbery. This was a whole new world.

I did not speak too much I just watched and observed everything around me. Once I was processed I was shuffled through to the next stage that was a big holding area where you get allocated to a cell and see a doctor.

I got the drift that I and all in the waiting area would not be taken to the landing and cell, until around half ten that night. I was given my bed pack and in I went to sit and wait.

I looked around at all of the occupants but, stopped and stared in disbelief, it was my elder brother who I had been brought up with. He was really my uncle but I have always looked at him as a brother, he had been around since I could remember, what was he doing here? This had to be his double! It wasn't, it couldn't be him! It was him.

I went right over to him and he was more concerned about what had happened with me. I quickly told him about the sentence and demanded to know what the hell he was doing in prison. He had never been in a prison.

He told me he had attended my trial that morning and the police were giving my family a hard time outside the court, trying to intimidate my family members. He said they just walked over to him in the court doorway and arrested him for non-payment of a fine. He explained he was given a fine for a motoring offence two years previously and had not paid it.

What a time for them to do that, I hope they were pleased with themselves, I detested them. He went on to say the police took him straight to Huyton Magistrates court and put him before a bench of magistrates.

He told them he had forgotten about the fine and he would pay in full on the following Friday out of his wages. They would not accept it and sent him to prison for fourteen days, they had even refused to accept a cheque, nor would they let him make a phone call to his works boss to bring his wages money into the courts. He could loose his job.

He felt it was already mapped out before he even appeared in the court. This did not surprise me after what I had experienced so far myself. Why were the police doing this to my family, my uncle Stephen (Stephen Gavin), was no use to anyone in prison. I decided to go and see the warder to see if I could get a phone call, try get him bought out but I was kidding myself, there was not a chance.

I would have to wait and see the probation service or the priest, they were helpful in prisons. I asked the warder if it would be possible to put us in the same cell. He said he would see. I left the warder to it and went back in the cell waiting room. Billy had come through and I introduced him to Stephen. Billy had seen him at our court appearances.

I caught hold of the vicar on the way through by chance and asked him if he could call my mother or aunt Pam and let them know where Stephen was. The vicar said he would try but it could be the following day. I told him I appreciated the call and he went on his merry way. That was the good thing about the vicar and probation service, they would always try to help out if they could.

All three of us ended up in the same cell that night. We talked all through the night and had a good laugh. Stephen did not want to tell me much about what was going on outside but I eventually got it all out of him, he was not a hard nut to crack.

He enlightened me on all the family, he told me that my mum and dad had moved back to Roby, they had bought a new house, a great big one in Church

Road. The house was not to far from Huyton Village. He said that my dad was still working and not doing to bad. It was all very nice to hear but I knew most of that already, it was the headaches I wanted to know about.

He told me that there had a been some difficult times and that there was lots of gossip. Basically my mother had fought to stay in Huyton and had succeeded. She would not be "ran out of town", as some would have liked people to believe.

My mother was making herself ill with worry over what the police were doing to me. That was the main problem out there in the outside world, it was breaking her down. Although I assured her I was fine every time I see her on a visit she still stressed herself out.

I joked to Stephen that I would give her a nice Xmas present, I would be getting released on Christmas Eve. He thought that would be the best thing that could happen for her.

It was true, my earliest release date was Xmas eve. I just had to behave. We talked on through the night and fell asleep in the very early hours of the next morning. I had learned quite a bit from Stephen and relished in the thought that I would soon be back in reality. The police had threatened my mother with promises of putting me in prison for a very long time.

The next day we went out on to the exercise yard and had a walk, it was the only time we were to get out the cell. I got to see the vicar after we had spent an hour walking around in little circles. He promised me he would call my mother or aunt Pam and took the phone numbers. He said he would let them know where Stephen, their brother was. They had put him in prison and I just couldn't get my head around him being there, each time I looked around.

It was just madness. No matter where I looked he was there and I felt responsible. It was the next day after that when the door opened and the warder asked for Gavin to pack all his kit as he was to be released.

I felt an urge to become Stephen Gavin, it dawned on me that I could do it. I could just pretend to be him, I knew all his details and we looked pretty similar, short dark hair and the similar features that most families show. Should I?

For the split second it crossed my mind, the trouble it would have caused pulled me back to reality. He was around Eight years older anyway. It was great to see him go, I gave him a big hug and told him to take care, Billy did to. I sent my love to my family and wished all at home my best.

It must have taken me a week to get over the shock of him being in prison. A couple of weeks passed and we got familiar with some of the other inmates and learned of their activities in crime and the stories carried on about the corrupt way the system was being run.

It seemed that every one was innocent walking

around the jail. Every single person I spoke to had a grievance of some sort with the system, most of the tales I found amusing.

One or two I took interest in as I thought their predicaments had valid points. It was all education and to learn from other peoples misfortunes could not be more interesting.

# CHAPTER SIXTEEN
## POLICE HASSLE AND TRANSFERS

It seemed every one was waiting for an appeal hearing and would be going home soon, everyone was innocent! I soon come to terms with the prison way of life. I was on the exercise yard when I was called for a special visit. This was a legal visit, non-family. Billy was called to. We went along with the warder and we waited in the waiting room patiently until we got called into the visiting room. Exercise was just finishing so it didn't matter to us, we were out the cell for a little longer.

I got called in first. I entered the room and it was the police from Southampton. I asked what they wanted and they asked me if I had anything to say about the Robbery in Southampton. I told them that I had no comment to make and went to walk out the room. They called the warder and handed him a piece of paper, they asked the guard to serve it on me, as they did not want to get too close.

I was amazed at the actions of them and refused to accept the piece of paper, I then walked out the room. I told the warder if they come back I want my solicitor present, that these policemen I did not want near me. I had took an instant dislike to the two C.I.D. who talked like farmer Giles and his pet dog. Their accents were very odd, they did not speak proper English.

I didn't want to know and I was not entertaining these two after the I.D Parade carry on. No, I wanted my solicitor, I had rights. I demanded to be taken to my cell. I could not see Billy in the waiting room, I wondered what was happening to him, was he getting the same hassle? These coppers were off their heads, surely. Why couldn't they just leave us alone, I had nothing to do with their investigation and didn't ever want to go to their shitty little town. I was getting sick to death with the name of it.

I was getting frustrated and realised I was showing aggression. This was not like me to get worked up so easily. I was placid, I was laid back and open minded or at least I used to be. The prison was starting to have an effect on me. I was definitely not myself anymore, I was changing and I felt it in that instant, I had put my foot down.

There was now a few warders about and one in particular started to raise his voice at the C.I.D. He was telling them that he did not care who they were, they're now in his prison and rules were rules, they had no rights in this establishment and if the inmate did not want to be interviewed, they could not make him.

I was escorted back to the wing and in to my cell. I was pleased that the warders had a go at them. I sat waiting for Billy and then began pacing the floor. It was only the standard twelve-foot by eight-foot room with a bunk bed. I heard the familiar bouncing of feet coming along the landing and the all to familiar jingle of keys. The door opened and in walked Billy.

He looked white. I could tell instantly that he had something on his mind. The door slammed behind him and he told me what had happened. The C.I.D. had seen him in the interview room and tried to question him again, he had asked for a solicitor when they passed him a piece of paper, he told me he did not say a word he just stared at the wall. He refused to accept the paper as well. He told the police that if they want any communication with him they would have to go through his solicitor.

The law states that the inmate's solicitor should accompany him on an interview from police whilst in custody. It is an illegal approach and against procedure. I had learned quite a bit whilst spending time in prison. The whole incident left both of us with bitter tastes in our mouths. It took several hours for the both of us to stop thinking and talking about it. After all not much else happened during our days locked in the cell. That day was different. A few hours later and it was forgotten.

It was during the fourth week, early in the morning

around five thirty when our door opened and we were told to pack as we were getting transferred to another prison, it did not shock either of us but did surprise us. We were on the move. There was a lot of over crowding in the prison and this was a normal practice to be taken at short notice to another less crowded prison.

It was a day out and we would get to go on the coach sight seeing for an hour or so.

We got our kit together and were taken to reception. There we would be told where we would be going. I expected a prison called Kirkham or something like that, an allocations officer had told me I was a category 'C' prisoner earlier. That meant I would go to a more open prison.

Kirkham was a category 'C' open prison, where you could go through the re-habilitation process, in order to ready your self for the outside world. That amused me because Billy only had a couple of weeks until his release date, he just about had enough time to have a shit and a shave. We got changed into our civilian clothes and that felt good.

We then grabbed some breakfast. The breakfast was lovely, grilled sausages, two fried eggs and slithers of sizzling bacon, fried bread and beans. It was looking good, I had a good imagination and always pictured the bowl of porridge to something nice, it never quite tasted like a proper breakfast. It was as rotten as usual. There was no such thing as good food in prison.

My name was called so I made my way to the desk to be told of my allocation. Wandsworth prison! I told him he must have made a mistake, I couldn't be going to London. He then told me that when I get there I would be transferred to another jail. Well, I had heard that when you upset the prison department you could find yourself at the other end of the country but, I had kept my head down and caused no problems. Why should I be going there?

Billy then got called and he returned with the same location as me. This was out of order, Billy said it didn't matter because they couldn't change time and he only had a few weeks to go. I had only a few months left so let them send us where they want. He had a good point and I agreed, let's not get too down about it we had to keep strong.

The trip to Wandsworth was interrupted by one stop at the Birmingham prison. This was to go to the toilet and pick a few transfers up. It was called Winson Green, it was not the Hilton hotel I can say that. There were a lot of rumours floating around that a couple of inmates had been kicked to death whilst in custody there. We were there for a long hour, then back on the bus. Now we headed for London right down the M1. Thank god we didn't have to spend the night in there.

We got into Wandsworth after a tour of Hyde Park, Mayfair and the Vauxhall Bridge. It was nice to see some of the sights. London looked a nice place in the early evening. We went through the usual formalities except we did not need to wear prison uniform, as we were to be transferred to Winchester Prison the next morning.

So this is where our true destination was. We went to a cell crashed out and were up and back in reception for Six Thirty. We were on the bus by seven thirty and travelling to the town of Winchester. I still could not work out why we got allocated here. It was handy for Billy as it was around twelve miles from Southampton.

He would now be ok for a visit, he could not get many, as he didn't have long to go. I was a long way from home. Well we got there and were told that we would be finishing our sentences off there, they did not know why we were sent there, they seemed more surprised than ourselves. We went through the same old rigmarole as before, changing, seeing a doctor and so on before we got put on the wing. We were in the same cell again, we were tired from the journey and had an early night.

# CHAPTER SEVENTEEN
## CHARGED WITH A ROBBERY

The next morning I was told that I had a solicitors visit. This was strange, as I did not expect a visit from anyone, it was out of the blue. I went along and was introduced to a small man in his thirties with a beard and short curly hair with a bald patch. I asked him why he had come to see me and he told me that Paul Rooney had called him, asking for him to represent me on a police visit later that afternoon.

I was confused, I asked him what was it about and he explained to me, the police that came to see me in Liverpool from Southampton wanted to see me again. I was pissed off with these people and told the solicitor that I would refuse to see them. He told me that was allowed but he would have to see them anyway, to see why they wanted to interview me, he knew that I had nothing to say to them.

That afternoon, I was called back to the special visits rooms where I talked to the solicitor again. He told me that they had to see me so they could arrest and charge me with a Robbery. My whole life stopped in an instant. I asked him to repeat it again, I was not hearing right and I was not dreaming, this was really happening. I was asked to go into the room where the police were, the solicitor and two warders accompanied me as I entered.

The C.I.D. said his name again D.C. Essary, he cautioned me, (read me my rights) told me he was charging me with Robbery of the Seaweed Public house, in Southampton. He then asked if I had anything to say in response to the charge. I did, I told him I have done no Robbery and knew nothing of any Robbery and they must be mad.

I was then given a court date to appear at Southampton magistrates court a few weeks later. I was given a piece of paper and told it was a charge sheet, it was exactly the same piece of paper they had tried to give me in Walton Jail. I tried to tell them they had got it wrong, all very wrong, they were barking up the wrong tree. I looked at them in disgust, Essary smirked. I went to a different room with the solicitor and asked him what was going to happen.

I was told that I could try for an Old Style Committal, which was a pre-trial at the magistrates. There he said we could listen to the evidence and then it could be thrown out. I went on to explain about the I.D Parade in Liverpool and the way it went. The Robbery was nothing to do with me and I didn't know shit about anything in Southampton so, how could there be any evidence?

The solicitor looked at me like I was an idiot, I asked him if he believed me and he said that he believed that I may not have done the Robbery but, he could not quite believe the I.D Parade carry on. I told him it may be hard to believe but he should talk to Mark at Rooney's office, he said he would do that.

I also told him that he was obviously accustomed to the usual criminals telling him a load of cods wallop but not to confuse me with that type. I had nothing to do with Robbery's or anything similar.

I then went back to my cell very, very, very confused. I could not work this out, I just could not understand it. Billy was out of the cell somewhere and I just sat on the bed in a bit of a trance. I could have put my finger in a plug socket and I would not have felt it. What were they doing to my head, this was getting to be too much. I was not a Robber.

Billy was back, he just looked at the window, he threw his charge sheet on the bed next to mine, he did not have to say a word. We were taken to the courts a few weeks later and put before the local magistrates. We were both remanded in custody although we were both already in custody. Billy was due for release and this meant that Billy would not be getting released on his discharge date.

The warders came in the cell on the morning of Billy's release and took him to reception, changed his clothes and took him on to the remand wing. This was a great strain on the both of us and it took at least a week for us to function normally again. We were remanded for months on the charge and it seemed to drag on forever.

The committal was not as we had expected and we ended up waiting for a trial at the Crown court. I was given a copy of the depositions, this was all the statements to be used by the prosecution. I studied them hard and read every bit of literature in the stack of paper work. I could not help but get even more confused trying to read the case against me.

There was several statements made by lots of people and some of them had made up to seven different sworn statements in the space of almost a year. They clashed with what was said in their earlier statements and contradicted themselves time and time again. They were clearly changing their first statements to suit, in the second, third and fourth statements.

I had a hard time getting the stories and facts in order. Since I was a little kid I had loved a puzzle and this was a massive puzzle, not a game. There was also a typed statement from a girl called Jackie Kelly, she said she knew me and knew I had done the Robbery! I could not work this out, it was like hitting a brick wall at a hundred miles an hour. Who the hell was this girl? I was staring at a proper frame up! This was not real.

This could not be happening, for god's sake

someone get me out of here. I had a mind full of confusion and was walking around a bit on the down side. I just could not believe that the police were serious. They were actually following this through and it was all lies and impossibilities, surely they could not be serious? Could they?

I had been able to get in the gym most days. That helped me to keep on functioning, healthy body healthy mind. I was in the gym when a skinhead seemed to be lurking about near my weight bench, I nodded a hello to feel him out. He could have been having a rest but he seemed too close for comfort. He had a face like a bulldog chewing a wasp and did not seem friendly at all, I was not about to pat this one on the back and tell him to fetch.

He carried on sitting there chewing on gum or someone's ear, staring at me as if he would like to chew on one of my ears. I asked him what was up and he stood up, pulled his shoulders back and growled at me that he had a message for me. I thought he was going to throw a punch. I lined him up and stood in a position to defend myself, one foot forward and my arms half raised and at the ready.

He must have sensed it and told me he was not there for a fight but had something to tell me about the Robbery I was up in court for. He said we should link up on the exercise yard and it would be for my own good, I agreed to the meet. Strange little chap I thought.

There were quite a few Skins on the wing but this one was the one that looked like a proper raving lunatic. I wondered what this bald psycho had to offer me.

I got on to the exercise yard and found the skin waiting for me. His name was Mickey Webb, he was a proper lunatic. I had asked a couple of the other inmates who he was, they had told me a few stories about him and it was confirmed that he was a little nutter. I knew most of the inmates by now and there was not a lot that went passed without me knowing about it. I walked up to Mickey and asked him what he had to say.

Well, he went on to tell me that the skins were friends of one of the witnesses in my case, Jackie Kelly. I was wide-awake, I was all ears. He told me she had approached a brother (another Skinhead) and told them that she had not made a statement, she was not going to go to court against me.

I replied that I would prefer it if she did go to court and tell the bloody truth. I could not believe what I was hearing. I told Mickey that I didn't even know her, I didn't have a clue about the Robbery and that if I got framed for it by the police why couldn't it happen to others. This had to be exposed for what it was. This friend of theirs Jackie Kelly knew it.

It was no good people running away from it, even if they did have drug problems. He had mentioned that the girl was on drugs at the time of her arrest and still was. How was I involved with these people, how did I end up in this mess? My head was going and I felt anger rising through my body, I turned to Mickey and told him to go back to his people and ask them why they were sending him to me.

He then went on to explain that it was Jackie Kelly, she wanted to visit me to talk to me and explain herself, she could not live with it, she was in a mess. He said it could be possible for her to speak with me if I was to get a visit the same day as him, she could then swap on the visit and talk to me face to face.

I did want an explanation from her and not from a third or fourth hand conversation. I just wanted to know why? From her mouth. Who was this girl who names me as a Robber, who doesn't even know me and then wants absolution, the cheeky bastards. I was not sure if I wanted to see her. I made my point and ended the conversation.

I walked around for the remainder of the exercise period alone. I was in no mood for chit chat or idle banter, I was in no mood for anything. The little chat had made me wake up, I had to talk to Billy. I met up with him the next day and told him what had been said, he was ready to go off his head as he also had been named by Jackie Kelly.

He said to me that to go on a visit and see her would not be a good idea but, at the same time it could give us the answers as to what was going on. I said, to be prepared in the court, would be in our favour and we cannot expose the police properly without some inside knowledge. It was set then, a visit was to be arranged.

I sat in my cell awake all night thinking of the different scenarios that were possible, maybe it was all a set up, maybe it was to charge me with interfering with a witness. Who knew? I certainly didn't. My mind was running wild with the could and could be's, I just couldn't sleep. This was a difficult situation.

I thought to myself that I could not be interfering with a witness because I had not talked to her yet. I would not tell her what to do, as that would constitute some sort of interference. She was approaching me I was not approaching her. I cannot take a chance and say anything silly or stupid to her, can't loose my head and shout at her.

What was I thinking? Prison was definitely turning me insane. I came to the conclusion that there was nothing I was going to do, was or could be wrong. Then it dawned on me that she may not come, she may get cold feet and not turn up on a visit. She may just run off and never be seen again. She may just be working with the police, how would I know, how could I know? Was it all a big conspiracy? I just had to wait and see. I was in the hands of fate.

I saw Mickey the skin again a few days later and he told me that he had passed a message on that I would see her. He told me he and his brothers would help me as much as they could, they even felt sorry for me. I told him it was not sympathy I wanted, it was justice. This was big, it was my life that was in the balance.

All that went through my head was the thought of the police actually thinking that they could get away with fitting me up. Who was they to play 'God' and decide who shall be going to prison, who the fuck did these coppers think they were?

They cannot just fit someone up for a robbery and go through with it. Brush it under the carpet as if nothing was wrong. What was going on in this country? Was it accepted by the government for this carry on to be allowed? I had a terrible nights sleep that night.

# CHAPTER EIGHTEEN
## OLD FLAMES AND FRIENDS

During my stay at Winchester I had a couple of visits from my girlfriend Tracey law. The last visit was the worst. Pressures of everything were to be too much for her to take. We parted on a good note. I was gutted but I knew we had to part for her sake. She had been getting grief back in Huyton and had gone to stay with her sister in Bath.

She was a beautifully natured girl and was very placid, she was around five foot five with long black curly hair, a lovely face and a smile that would brighten up any dull day. She had beautiful eyes and perfect white teeth. We had been happy together and only had eyes for each other. We had travelled to visit her sister Pauline in Holland and stayed for a few weeks in a small place in the South, called Roermond.

We had loved it so much there that upon my release we had planned to live there. She had lost a baby just before my arrest, she'd had a miscarriage and she was determined to try again once I was out. She had fixed it with her brother in law Wiel, so that I would be working over there in Holland. It looked quite possible that we would be living there very soon.

Her mum Maisey and dad Bobby were normal, nice and hard working people, even her little sister Rosey was nice and they were a good family. I was approved I think, because I used to go to their house after work in the work van. It was good for them to see that their daughter was with a worker and not a scallywag.

My family also liked her, we all got on very well, normality. The pressures of the whole escapade meant that I did not know for sure when I would be released so I could not give her a time or date, I was in the hands of the system. Her family were all putting pressure on her to forget me as I was too much trouble, I could only agree with them and we had to let go.

It was a sad time but I did not want her to have this life, she deserved better and I wanted her to move on and get somewhere in life, I did not want her to suffer my fate. We had some great times together and not many bad ones but all the memories were nice, even a serious car crash on the motorway.

A car had moved into us on the motorway one evening and as we went into a skid before crashing, she just looked at me and held my hand saying she was coming with me. The car I was driving was a hired car a friend had hired, his name was Brian Peter's.

Tracey and I had been closer than close. She cried and left the visiting room, that was to be the last time I saw her. I clenched my fist and cursed the system. I had to let her go. I had been receiving regular letters from all my family and quite a few mates. I was never short of getting a letter but, now I would be missing the letters from Tracey and they were special. I had an empty feeling that would not be filled in a hurry that was for sure.

There was another mate of mine, who I knew was living near Bournemouth, his name was Jeff Maines. His family were from Huyton, we had known each other all our lives. He had always been a good laugh we had stayed in touch while I was in prison. He was always dropping me a line encouraging me to be positive and strong, he would visit any time I ever wanted.

It was the quality of a proper mate. I had sent him a letter asking him to visit. It had been a while since I had seen him, it would be good to catch up on things, good to see him to. He was due to visit that week. I looked forward to seeing him.

The very thought of seeing him made me smile as he was very funny and always having a good laugh. You see about a year and a half ago I was in Bournemouth. I was working at a hotel doing Silver Service waiting on, at a five star hotel called the Carlton Hotel and one day a few of the lads turned up from Liverpool.

It was Gary Smith known as Eno, a big lad and related through my dad's family. Tony Davies, he was a very short fella with great big glasses, his dad Butch I had known all of my life. He was hilarious when he had a lager down his neck. The third was Jeff Maines.

Well, we all got in the car and I directed them to a place on the other side of the town, as we travelled along Jeff was driving and having an argument with Gary. It was funny, I giggled in the back, Gary kept telling Jeff he couldn't drive and was giving him lots of stick. He was really trying to wind Jeff up.

Jeff was saying that he had driven safely all the way from Liverpool without an accident and Gary was telling me how many times he had come close to death on the journey, Then Tony would pipe in for them to shut up and for Jeff to watch the road and stop turning around, trying to tell us his side of events. It was comical.

Jeff had black hair in an Afro style, with a thick moustache, typical stereotype scouser. I was giggling away when Jeff slammed the brake on. I almost swallowed my cigarette. He was roaring away about how good his driving was and if Gary wanted to walk he could. I looked out the window and still laughing, I mentioned that Jeff had stopped in the middle of a road junction. It would be best if we moved and done it quickly. As there were a lot of motorists heading our way.

Jeff got to the other side of the junction while the cursing and arguing carried on, it was hilarious I was getting a stitch with so much laughter, it was like a scene from T.V. Gary was now going on about petrol but, each time Jeff spoke he would accelerate then turn to us and talk, he was not looking where he was going but at me and Tony in the back.

Gary shouted for Jeff to watch the bike. Jeff turned then swerved out the way and stated that he was the best driver in the car and that if it was any of us lot driving we would have knocked him over. Gary mentioned the fact that if he were watching the road he would not have had the situation in the first place. This was a road trip this one. I couldn't stop laughing, I saw another cyclist ahead and Jeff seemed to get too close for comfort, we all had a go at him.

For us to get to our destination in one piece would be an achievement, Jeff was a terrible driver. We came to a junction in Branksome Park and I told him it was one of those turns where he would have to be quick and get over sharpish, as there was a bend to the right hand side where traffic would come flying past so he would have to put his foot down.

He said that it was no problem and started to edge out, waiting to take his opportunity and join the traffic and head right. He kept on edging out and the traffic coming from the right was having to swerve out of his way. We saw a cyclist come flying around the corner at speed and we all told Jeff to watch out for him.

As the cyclist crossed our front Jeff edged out a bit more. The cyclist swerved out of the way nearly hitting an on coming car. He screamed some obscenities at Jeff and his driving. Jeff decided to put his head out the window and shout at him, saying he should be watching the road mixed with a few obscenities.

Both Tony and myself were in the back curling up in hysterics at the nutty situation and Gary was holding his head with both hands in the front, shouting to Jeff that the car was still moving forward. Jeff was not listening, he was to busy hanging out the window telling the cyclist what he thought of him, no one could get his attention.

There was a bang, a loud crunching noise and a stifled sort of moan. We all stared in front of us mouths agape and in astonishment. There was a man dressed in black wearing a helmet flying acrobatically right the way across the bonnet, in mid air. I could see the expression on his face, it was like slow motion and he did not look amused.

It was deathly silent and the scooter rider landed in a thundering heap about eight yards to our left on the pavement. I muttered, "oh fuck!" and looked at the others, I then went into a fit of uncontrollable laughter. I know it was not funny but this was too much of a pantomime. Jeff just stared at the heap on the floor with a dazed sort of look.

The man on the floor slowly got to his feet and dusted himself down as we all looked on in amazement, he was not full of broken bones and he seemed alright.

His scooter would need some attention but the main thing was that he was ok. Jeff broke the silence and slowly got out the car.

He said to the man that he should have had his eyes on the road and should have been watching where he was going. He said to the man it was his own fault and deserved it. He carried on and was telling the fella that he had better not have done damage to his car, he told him what a stupid person he was to ride a scooter and he should be a normal person and get a car just like him. Jeff was from another planet.

I couldn't believe my ears I could only hold my stomach with the pain of laughter. Gary got out the car and directed Jeff back to the passenger side, he would not be driving again that day even if it were his own car. Tony looked at me and said to look at what he had to put up with all the way down from Liverpool.

Gary asked the bloke if he was ok and if he could help him in anyway, the victim refused any help saying he was ok and he could sort himself out. I think he just wanted to see the back of Jeff's car and the nutter's in it. Gary told the scooter rider to take no notice of Jeff as he was in shock from the accident.

That was Jeff then but he had come on since then. He had bought a flat near Eastleigh Airport, got a good job that paid well and was doing well for himself. His job was driving a van for some big demolition company in Hampshire. I looked forward to seeing him. He was a true friend.

## CHAPTER NINETEEN
## TWO WEEK VISIT FROM
## THE UNEXPECTED

I was called out to the visiting room. There was Jeff with his nephew Kenny. There was twenty-five cups of tea on the table and around twenty bars of chocolate. I shook hands and sat down looking curiously at all the cups of tea. I was puzzled and asked what all the cups were for, Jeff said it saves going back to the kiosk to get more as it will waste the time.

I told you he was from a different planet did I not. I nodded and laughed. He told me how things were out there in the world and how he was doing. He was doing well and I was pleased for him, he asked how my family were and I told him all I knew. He asked about Tracey and I told him, he told me I was punishing myself and should stay in touch with her, as in his eyes we suited each other.

He cheered me up by telling me I would be home in no time at all. The trial for the Robbery would be over and I would be proved innocent. He told me everyone knew it was a frame up. I hoped he was right.

I told him about Jackie Kelly. He said to me I was doing the right thing and that maybe it was true that she didn't write the statement. I told him I was keeping an open mind and he agreed.

I told him about the I.D. Parade up in Liverpool. He was amazed. He could not believe it. He said he had heard the rumour but didn't think it was possible to be true. I told him I needed a solicitor from outside of Southampton, I was too paranoid to have one from that same area. He told me he would try to help and see if he could find a good one for me.

We talked about family things and what he was doing at work then the visit came to an abrupt end. Well at least the visit finished on a good note whilst the time had flown by as we chatted. I shook Jeff and Kenny's hands, I thanked them both for coming up to see me. All the visitors left the visiting room and went back to their lives of normality. Jeff was a proper mate.

A few days later Mickey the skin asked for a word in private, so I invited him into my cell and asked how I could help. He told me that his friend had come into prison for a two-week vacation for fines, would it be ok to have a chat with him, he was Jackie Kelly's friend? I said yes and told him there was to be no trouble from me, I think they must have thought that I would have blamed them just because they knew her.

I met up with the baldy chap on the exercise yard. He shook my hand and stated his name was Ray. He told me everything he knew and I was shell-shocked. What he was telling me must have been difficult to say to his own mates, but to me it must have been even harder.

He went into detail about the times Jackie Kelly had confided in him, he explained that she was from a good back ground and a decent family but got mixed up with drugs. He knew I did not know her as she had told him everything. She felt she needed to talk to me as she could not live with the guilt of what she had done.

I thanked him for not telling anyone the full velocity of what he knew, this was something that if done properly would expose the police, they were corrupt. They were bad, they were a disgrace and they needed to be shown for what they really were. I asked him how much he trusted Jackie Kelly and he told me one hundred percent.

I asked if he could be on the visit with her as I did not trust things and I thought I might be getting trapped, he assured me that it was no set up. He told me Jacky Kelly was nervous about coming in to see me and would she be safe, she didn't know me and the police had portrayed me as a psychopath, she did not believe it but, needed that bit of assurance that there would be no trouble for her, if she was to come in on a visit.

I explained to him I was not about to show any frustration to the one and only person that held my liberty in their hands nor, was I the violent nutter they led her to believe I was. He told me that she was having a hard time living with it all, I agreed, but not as hard a time as what I was having. He said she was really a nice person, I assured him once again that I was too but, had trouble sleeping.

A visit would be arranged and I gave him my word that I would not add to her stress, I would be there to listen. I left Ray on a good note, he seemed to have his morals in order. I tried to think of how it must be being Jackie Kelly. Ray had told me she did not do drugs anymore, this had at least had a good effect on someone but I was not convinced. I didn't really care about her problems, I was more concerned about my own problems. She had come into my life and the police, put me in her life and I was the one suffering.

It was a week later when Ray told me she would come up, he would be out of prison and he would visit a friend of his, Mickey. I should arrange a visit the same afternoon we could exchange visitors and then I would be able to listen to her. He told me this was all unbelievable and beyond belief but, this was the only way to do it without anyone else knowing. I agreed. It had to be undetected.

# CHAPTER TWENTY
## CONFRONTATION POLICE STYLE


On my committal for trial at the magistrates court there had been an incident. Billy and myself had been taken to the magistrates and taken in to the cells separately. As I had got off the bus my solicitor was there and asked me if I was prepared to go on an I.D.Parade. I told him I was prepared to attend as long as he was present and made notes of everything.

He smiled and assured me that the I.D.Parade in Liverpool would never happen again, he was more than sure. I was taken to the cells to await the court appearance. The police came to the cells and told me we were going, I thought it was to court but they led me handcuffed through a corridor and then into a sort of courtyard.

A door opened and a lot of police walked in stood either side of the door and then a youngish looking girl looked at me. I looked at her and as quick as she looked at me she turned away, I remember thinking who the hell is that and it made me suspicious. I was then taken back to the cell, I asked the police what the hell was going on and was told to shut up and pushed in to the cell that I came from.

When I went up to the court my solicitor was over to the dock, he told me that the Inspector had ordered a confrontation with a witness because I had refused to attend an I.D.Parade. I was flabbergasted. You could have knocked me over with a feather. I told him about what had happened and he told me not to worry he would deal with it.

The prosecution applied to enter further fresh evidence in the form of an I.D Parade, a positive identification. The inspector was then sworn under oath and told a cock and bull story. My world got worse, another person I did not know had apparently said I was a Robber. My solicitor then decided to tell the magistrate that the Inspector was out of order and had just committed an illegal action.

He demanded that it could not be used as evidence as he had notified the Inspector that I was very willing to attend a formal I.D. Parade and that the Inspector had broken the rules. He also demanded a copy of the new statement from the young girl, he was given the copy and read it quickly. He then looked at me and nodded as if asking for permission to do something, I nodded back in hope.

He turned to the magistrates and told them the positive Identification of me was not the person described, she had described Billy with his fair hair and then stated it was Tony Allan, she then went on to name Billy Willis with his dark brown hair and described me. He then said he needed a decision from the magistrates if they were going to allow it to be used as evidence under a certain act of law.

They stated they would be passing it in its present form and letting it be used at the trial. He stood there like a Yorkshire Terrier and told them that he could not continue in the case as my solicitor, he was now a witness to an illegal act and a blatant lie by an Inspector under oath. He was truly disgusted and told them so.

He would see all in the Crown Court. He had won my admiration but I still had no freedom. I was getting down with one thing or another and I did not want to be there, this girl did not know me, it was impossible, yet there was a statement. Now I was left without an acting solicitor on my own. He had just resigned to be my witness.

The solicitor gathered his papers and left the court. It was a very bold move by a solicitor and them sort of people are few and far between. I thanked God once again, maybe there was hope. Although some what disappointed in the proceedings I felt a warmth in the knowledge that the stupid and sneaky police were not as clever as they thought, they were leaving a murky trail like a snail, to expose them into total embarrassment should not be to difficult.

Even an idiot could see it. Surely the judge would

see right through the lot of it, I had faith in a judge but in nothing below that status. It was looking ever so likely that I would not be at home for this Xmas coming up.

Some time later I met with my new solicitors. I met with Robert Renshaw, he was very tall, very slim and came across to me as a genuine solicitor, he was ok, he was good. I went through everything with him each morning for around three days. I had to tell him every detail I could think of and remember.

He was going to instruct a barrister and wanted my permission to choose one whom he had faith in, the man for the job he said. I agreed and told him that I trusted his judgement. He told me his name would be Paul Garlick, he was a junior barrister. He would arrange a couple of visits for me with him at the prison. He had read all the evidence to be used against me and he was not convinced that I should have been charged.

The only evidence was the statement by Jacky Kelly, he was shocked to see that the original statement had not been served on us, all we had was a type written one and a very suspicious one at that. There was also a new statement from a woman stating that she picked me out in Liverpool on a I.D.Parade, she had added that she recognised my eyes and said I was talking with a Liverpool accent and was of the same build.

In her original statement she said the one with the accent similar to a Liverpool one was wearing a scarf across his face and was short and stocky. It looked like each time she written a statement it became more and more obvious that it was directed at me. I asked Renshaw if she was allowed to do this, he said it was but only if there is something new to add, this one had stated in her first statement that the Robber wearing the full-face balaclava attacking her husband was a local as she could tell by his accent.

Amazing how a few months later it appears as a Liverpool accent. The confrontation at the police station was also leaving a lot to be desired considering the way it all happened, plus we had received a statement from the solicitor who was with me at the confrontation in Southampton and one from the solicitors clerk in Liverpool. It sort of cancelled the dodgy evidence out, basically the only evidence, was nothing!

There were fibres found by the forensic team but none of it matched me. There were footprints and none of it matched me. The lot of it was like a sick joke, it would be a circus at the trial. There was nothing, it was all made up and manufactured by the police. I felt sickened that they had done this to me, it was like a sickness inside my body looking for a way out, it felt an urge to be let loose, something was building up inside me.

I was mentally cabbaged and just functioning on my nerves. I just wanted the trial date so I could get it out of my way, this was dragging on and I needed something to look forward to. I was in the dark and waiting. Well, Renshaw told me he would be in touch soon and let me know if he got the barrister of choice and let me know the date for the trial. It was turning into a joke, I could not believe they were carrying it on.

# CHAPTER TWENTY ONE
# CORRUPTION FROM
# THE HORSES MOUTH

I had my new solicitor visiting during the mornings as I was now waiting for my trial date to come and I was now happy with my new solicitor. He was from Bournemouth, his name was Robert Renshaw. I didn't exactly have a heavy schedule in the afternoons so the visit arranged to speak with Jackie Kelly was sorted out.

It was at the end of that week that I was to meet Jacky Kelly in the visiting room, I felt nervous for some reason. I was called out for a domestic visit and off to the visits room I went. I sat at the table waiting for my visitor and eyed everyone in the visiting room with suspicion.

The visitors all entered the room. I saw Kenny and he waved and shouted a big hello, Kenny was a funny lad and was very loud. It was good to see him. Jeff arrived at the table with him and we greeted each other as usual shaking hands and patting each other's back. He asked if all was ok and I just told him I did not know, he to was sceptical.

There was a few of the baldy mob getting visits and there were visitors still coming in. Jeff decided to start the betting about which one Jackie Kelly could be, before I knew it he was trying to bet me that a huge woman visiting a skinny little man was her, he had me laughing, then Kenny was asking if it really was her. I told him I did not think so because the little man was in for fraud and was from Salisbury.

I also knew she was going to be with one of the baldy boys. Jeff carried on saying it could be and before long Kenny was convinced that the big fatty was Jackie Kelly. I didn't think so but Kenny was a funny chap and had a heart of gold, up he got and went for more tea. As myself and Jeff talked we were looking around and trying to spot a signal from someone, we were not getting any indications from any one.

Then Kenny walked back towards us stopping at the big fatty's table and sat himself down with them. I said to Jeff that I would like to know what Kenny was doing and Jeff looked on in amazement. I started laughing, this could not be real, what had got into Kenny? After a couple of minutes Kenny got up shook their hands and came back to our table.

He sat down and said it was definitely not Jackie Kelly it was not her, the big fatty was named Sarah. He had sat down and introduced himself to the people and asked them their names, wished them all the best and made his leave. Job done he said, I laughed and found it amusing but told him not to go anywhere else. I didn't want this turning into a farce.

It was sometime later that a load more visitors walked in. I saw Ray and my heart started beating faster, I mentioned to Jeff that she must be here. I noticed a small girl with him she had very short mousy hair and it was longer at the front, sort of spiky. She was a Skinhead, a female one. As she talked to Ray she was looking over at us, it must have been her. As Ray went to sit down at a baldy's table he nodded to me indicating, to tell my visitors to get some tea. I asked Jeff to sit off for a bit and grab some teas with Kenny. They both left and joined the back of the tea queue.

The Skinhead girl was at the front of the queue and after she paid she picked up the drinks and headed for another table, I waited patiently for her to give the baldy's their tea then come over. I see Mickey the baldy had just entered the visits room and went straight over to the girl and kissed her, what the hell was going on I thought? Mickey had not mentioned to me he was Jackie Kelly's boyfriend I didn't know what to think, all kinds of things were running through my head now. This was turning into a drama.

My thought was interrupted by a really tall girl, she asked if she could have one of the chairs, I told her she could as there was one spare. She spoke in a soft voice and had a sheepish sort of smile, a nervous look on her face. I just looked the other way dismissing her presence, I wanted to see what was going on but this girl stood there a bit longer. I looked at her again and she sat down and went an embarrassing colour of red. I asked if her name was Jackie, she nodded and put her head down.

My god this girl looked nothing like what I had imagined I was shocked, I asked if she wanted a tea and she accepted like a very shy and timid person would. It was obvious that she was petrified. I broke the atmosphere and told her to relax and told her things are never as bad as they could be. I felt that I was telling her a lie because they really could not be any worse for me in the situation I was in.

Anyway I took her hand and told her that if she didn't want to speak she didn't have to, she was safe here and I knew she had been going through an ordeal. She looked up at me and into my eyes with a sort of innocence, tears at the ready, her hand was warm but trembling. I told her I was not the big bad monster the police had said I was.

She broke down and cried, her head down again and sobbing and sobbing and sobbing, I just said to let it out and don't worry, I didn't know what else to say, what could I say? Had I said the wrong thing? I cant handle girls crying, not like this, if she didn't stop soon I might just join in myself, this was getting very emotional.

I looked around to see if she was attracting much

attention but it seemed not. I looked over to the baldy's table but they were all having a laugh, Jeff and Kenny had joined them, they were all getting on like a house on fire. Their laughing was loud and they seemed to be having a right old giggle about something.

I asked Jackie if she wanted me to go and get her a tissue but she said it was ok, wiped her face and said sorry. I told her not to be and asked her how she was doing. I asked her about herself and tried to relax her. She seemed to be warming towards me, getting a bit of confidence. She went on to tell me what had happened at the police station and that she remembered signing a statement but not writing or reading it. She told me all she could remember and all the little details that she could think of.

She went on to tell me that she was away from drugs now permanently. I told her that she had to tell the truth in court, I asked her had she ever done this before, if she was paid by the police to give evidence, if she was a regular. She seemed hurt by my questions but I explained to her that I had to ask, I was sorry to insult her but I needed to know.

She promised she had never been in a situation like this and had not done it before, I think I believed her but my trust was a little non existent these days. I was in a terrible situation here, I had not even been to Southampton. Yet I was charged with a big bad Robbery there and the police seemed to be going out of their way to put me away.

She said she knew that I had not done the Robbery and she just wanted to put it right. Jeff interrupted and asked if we would like more teas, he called Jackie by her name and gave me an assured confirmation that she was who she said she was. It eased the paranoia and lowered the tensions, I declined the tea offer and so did Jackie.

She didn't know me and yet she seemed to have built some sort of trust up in me. I asked her if she was a policewoman under cover and was she wired up? She said she wasn't and asked me if I would like to check for a wire and frisk her down, I laughed and she did to. I told her it was ok I thought she was too young to be an under cover spy. Besides if she was the baldys would all lose my trust and respect.

I genuinely felt sorry for her but I was in no position to be sympathetic. She promised me she would not go back on to drugs and would come to court and tell the truth. I told her that being on drugs was just a phase in her life, which she had passed now, it was nothing to be ashamed of. It was really I suppose but, I didn't want to crumble her fragile world. She stood up and thanked me for listening.

She made her apologies once again and asked if she could stay in touch with me. I told her it would not be a good idea until after the trial or it could confuse the situation. She agreed and apologised saying that she felt so comfortable talking to me, that she felt she could lean on me for support. I told her I was a good listener and after this mess was sorted out I would get in touch but, she must stay away from the drugs. She smiled and nodded then left and walked over to the baldys table.

Jeff and Kenny were over to me in seconds. They asked if everything was ok. I told them that I felt sorry for her but, I couldn't believe that I had just spoken to the person who said I had done the Robbery. Jeff and I discussed the fact that we were both shocked by her appearance. We both expected a junky looking girl but Jackie was very clean and fresh looking and well dressed, as if she could be a someone. She was very shapely and had lovely long legs she quite pretty. How she ended up on drugs was unbelievable.

Well the visiting time was now over and all the visitor's had to make his or her way out. I said my good byes and watched the boys leave and followed their parting through the windows. My eyes caught Jackie Kelly's, she was waiting for my eyes to meet with hers. She had been waiting there looking at me and waiting for my gaze to go in her direction and catch my eye. I smiled and nodded to her, she gave the warmest smile I could of asked for and she waved and left. I sat and watched her walk away.

I noticed Ray the baldy and he nodded, smiled and put his thumb up in a questioningly way, I smiled and give him the thumbs up. Mickey come over to the table and asked if things were ok. I told him yes and he was pleased, I was getting to like this nutter. I spent that night thinking of Jacky Kelly, she would not leave my mind no matter how much I tried to think of other things. The effect of meeting her in person lasted for weeks. The next time I would see her would be at the trial. Who knows after that?

## CHAPTER TWENTY TWO
## ROBBER NUMBER THREE IN CUSTODY


It was a month or so before Xmas and Both myself and Billy were taken to the local Crown Court in Southampton for a plea. As we got into the crown court holding cells I was taken to see my Barrister, Bob Renshaw was there and introduced me to him, his name was Paul Garlick. He was to represent me.

The first thing he asked me was did I know the third man they had in custody? I didn't know anyone had been arrested. They told me they did not know his name yet but, they had been informed that he was picked out three times on an I.D Parade the day before, positively. He was due in the magistrates that same day. I looked at him and raised my eyebrows. I did not have a clue. I was sure to know who it was by the time I got back to the prison though.

He told me that he had read all the paperwork and had been filled in on everything by the solicitor. I gave him my view of what had gone on and he listened intensely, I told him all that I could remember. He seemed decent and very particular, he was around five foot nine of slim build with mousy brown shortish hair, he had normal features not sharp and sported gold-rimmed glasses.

He talked as though he could be a ruthless person to stand before in a trial. I just hoped so, he also explained to me that the prosecution were applying for a Red Robe Judge. He explained that this was only necessary in big Murder cases and big time Robberies, he also stated that a Red Robe Judge still had the power to hang someone.

This type of Judge had the most power above others. I said to him that I thought Hanging was abolished, he said it was but technically a person could still be hanged to this day for crimes against the Crown. I gulped and thought thank God I was not accused of something against the Queen, this was a horrible place and I didn't want to be here, I was scared.

The Barrister told me that he could see the prosecution were going way over the top and that would be their downfall, he told me that he knew I was innocent of the Robbery. That gave me some comfort for what it was worth.

We went into the court and there was a debate on where the trial was to be held. Both my barrister and Billy's barrister argued that it should be held out of the town of Southampton and the nearest court would be at the Old Bailey in London.

The local media had written several articles

concerning the Robbery that could have mis-lead any Jury member attending the trial, if they had read them. It was a valid point in my view and I did not think that, if a member of the Jury had read certain newspaper articles, I would get a Fair trial.

One newspaper article in particular stated that I, Tony Allan and Billy Willis had done the Robbery to get money for drugs. This was quoted in the local paper as from a police source. We had both been, "Hung Drawn And Quartered" by the media before we had even started the Robbery Trial. How can it be a fair trial with things like that in the papers?

The prosecution argued that Winchester Crown Court would be of a fair venue. The defence both stated that the twelve miles from Southampton to Winchester was not far enough also, that the local papers were of one and the same paper.

It was also mentioned that the victims had been running a pub in Winchester called the Ship Inn for years and the possibility of a juror having stopped there for a meal or a quick drink, was a bit on the dangerous side and should not be allowed. The likelihood was nothing short of obvious prejudism, considering there were not a lot of pubs in Winchester compared to a big town or city.

The Judge sitting said Winchester would be neutral and decided that the case merited a Red Robe Judge. I rolled my eyes and felt a sword through my stomach.

This was all a farce. It was not fair, nothing was and it was all a big stage play for them. How could it be a fair and honest trial with Juror's from the local area?

I looked at the prosecution in a lost sort of way and the words just came out my mouth. I said to him that if a person like myself could see through all this nonsense, how could such an educated man like himself go along with this fabrication knowing it was not justice.

He stood there in his black robe and wig staring at me as though I had slapped his hand. He was tall, over six foot and was of very sharp features with black greying short hair just showing around his ears. He was shaved blue. He sported a black sort of Onyx ring to his left little finger which I had noticed with curiosity, as he seemed to be wavering it about every time he spoke as if letting the world see he had one.

Something was not right here and I could smell something sinister behind this man. His name was De Sylva. He struck me as an evil being, as if he were a disciple of some sort. I could feel the tension between us as he stared at me. I was taken down the stairwell but I felt them eyes of De Sylva, burning into my back with a ferocity that could match the Devil himself. It was a very eerie experience, I felt shaken.

I sat in the cell until Bob and Paul came in to see me, they were both amused at my out break but sternly let me know that it would be best, not to do it again or the Judge would have me removed from the court and it would go on without me. It was legal to have the defendant removed from the court, they assured me of that.

I would be walking on hot coals when it comes to the trial, the thought of the trial terrified me. I couldn't handle a few hours in one of these courts never mind a bloody week. Paul explained to me that I would have to be represented by a Q.C. at the trial because of its higher bearing. I did not want to have to change representation and have to explain it all over again I was sick of it. They explained that Queens Council would be the final time I would have to give my explanation and I would have to go through most of. it with him.

I was tired, I was not feeling to good and my head was banging, all this was becoming too much to handle and stressing me out. I looked forward to getting back to my cell in the prison! What was coming over me?

Then it dawned on me, someone was nicked for the Robbery and would be going to the prison the same day. I couldn't wait to meet them. Who ever it was, my barrister was more than sure the police had got one of the Robber's as he had been pointed out three times. He had to be guilty, I had a few questions to ask the Robber and it wouldn't be friendly ones either.

# CHAPTER TWENTY THREE
## FRIEND OR FOE

I was back in my cell that night and had a very troublesome sleep. I was agitated and antagonising myself about what to say to him, the real Robber. Well the morning eventually came and Billy was calling me from the end of the landing. He was on the other side of the mesh fence. I went over to him and he told me that the Robber was one of my mates called Brian Peter's.

This could not be so, this was impossible, Brian was not a Robber. He was a worker not a thief he had been working in Bournemouth for years. He even had a family life and was married to a North East girl called Shirley with a few kids. I told Billy to go and get him.

He was back with Brian in seconds, it was really him, my god he could not be the Robber! I asked Brian what the hell was going on and he just looked at me and told me that he hadn't done it. He started crying and said that they had all pointed him out on the I.D. Parade. I shouted at him to get his head together and told him that Billy and myself were being set up as well. We had been going through this for almost ten months.

He sort of calmed himself down then got himself worked up again. I didn't need this so I said to Billy I would catch him later and to keep an eye on Brian. I also told Billy to find out every single thing that Brian knew, I was not convinced he knew nothing about the Robbery. Not until I could talk to him properly.

My brain was being fried while I was alive. If it was not Brian, that meant he must have had a dodgy I.D. Parade. I got to see him in the gym the next day and he told me all he knew. I knew Brian and I knew he was not really capable of the Robbery, he had convinced me more after a few questions.

I told him of my situation and what happened on my I.D. Parade, he was not surprised and believed it was a set up. I told him that there was now more evidence against him than anyone, he broke down again. I told him to pull himself together and crying like a fucking baby was not going to get him out of this. He must of known where he was on the night of the Robbery but he did not. It did not surprise me, how would anyone know where they were a few months ago? Never mind a whole year ago.

This was not good this was bad, very bad. With Brian being in the dock and me next to him it was not going to look good. I had been friends with Brian for years, I knew his mother, his brother and his sisters. I was so involved with Brian that we could have looked like best mates. We were not even talking up till this point.

We had fallen out with each other a while ago because I had crashed a car he had hired out from Bournemouth in Liverpool. It caused him a lot of headaches. No matter what, we would have to fight this in the dock together and his crying was not going to help. He seemed to be putting it on and looking for the attention, why I will never know.

This showed me just how much pull and power the C.I.D. had, it was frightening. I was more confused than ever now and this really puzzled me. Brian was a stocky little sort of, podgy bloke, around five foot ten. He also had a strong Liverpool accent, he had also been pointed out three times by all the witnesses at the pub, by those who were robbed.

I did not give Brian much hope here, I couldn't, they had sewn him up like a Kipper. I even had doubts about him myself, after all he was pointed out three times and during his questioning by the police he stated that he had never been to Southampton but they produced proof that he had been in Southampton some time ago.

He had attended a boxing presentation there. He had lied. Him being an amateur boxer with a string of fights to his name was not going to help him either, it would sink him for sure. So it put him in a very awkward spot. I didn't think he had done it but it kept niggling at the back of my head that it was possible. Very possible.

This was badly going worse for me. I felt the stress even more now. Brian did not have a clue what to do so I had to tell him to get a barrister real quick and tell his solicitor to dig into these C.I.D. dealing with us. There had to be something to fight with, as they cannot be getting away with this type of behaviour without leaving a clue for us.

They were bad coppers. Bad eggs completely. I would fight these bastards even if it killed me doing so. I had an image of Essary firmly lodged in my mind. He would not get away with this, no way, I knew about Jackie Kelly. I was slowly getting used to the fact that I had an ace card with her. It took me a few weeks to get used to the fact that Brian was charged with the Robbery. Three of us now in the hands of the system.

I was due for release from the criminal damage sentence and that was days away. It was Xmas, merry friggin Xmas. I had done my twelve months out of the eighteen, I had paid my dues. It was sickening enough getting the maximum sentence for a criminal damage charge, then to have to go through the humiliation of being discharged, then back into custody on the remand wing. More privileges were the only comfort I was to have.

I arrived on the remand wing and felt something like a celebrity, people on the wing were more than friendly and a lot of them expressed their sympathy's as to my plight, I was well respected and I could feel it. A lot of the prisoners were from Southampton and must have known we were innocent but what could anyone do about it? Nothing.

I had seen a lot of the inmates around the prison so it was not like going into a different prison. I went to the cell I was allocated and made my bed. Billy came in and passed me a lovely cup of tea, he was pissed off himself but we kept a brave face on and got on with the day. Brian was acting very strange but I put that down to depression, I would have to keep my eye on him in case he got suicidal which he seemed to be getting.

Billy told me he had seen Brian playing with a razor blade and when he asked him if he was ok, Brian told him that he was looking at his reflection in the metal. My head was bad enough but I told Billy that he was not as strong as we were and we would have to look out for him. Xmas passed without incident and into the New Year we went.

Brian tried every possible application for bail, right up to the high courts but to no avail, I told him he would have no chance. I thought it best not to tell Brian about Jackie Kelly. He kept disappearing from the wing and going missing for hours.

# CHAPTER TWENTY FOUR
## ROBBER NUMBER FOUR IN CUSTODY

I was told by one of the other inmates that Brian was going on special visits, seeing two men in suits. One of the suits was described as being of black hair and a moustache, the hairs on my back stood up. It didn't take an Einstein to figure out he must have been seeing the C.I.D. It had to be Essary. I asked Brian where he had been one day and he told me he had been to see a doctor but gave no indication as to his illness.

This I did not elaborate on, I just let him carry on with the lie. It appeared that some of my letters had gone missing and a lot of my paperwork to do with the trial went missing to. I told Billy and together we set a trap for Brian. We told him we were off to the gym and hid in another cell instead to watch and see if it was Brian. We now suspected him of working with the police for some unknown reason of his own.

We watched for an hour but nothing happened. We give it another ten minutes and give up. We both walked in on Brian as he sat in his cell. The door was closed over behind us and there was Brian, shifting through some paperwork on his bed. I asked him what they were for, thinking it was to do with our forth-coming trial.

He sort of panicked and threw them all together and put them in his locker. He was acting very odd as if he had done something wrong or had something to hide. He was reminding me of Judas himself, I thought of beating him and I could see that Billy was heading that way. I told Billy to hold off for the moment, lets have some answers here. It was like dealing with a rat of some sort, he had made my stomach turn, Billy was now frothing at the mouth, fuming. We knew he was up to no good. We just couldn't prove it.

Brian in a weasel type of way tried to explain himself, he told us that Essary the C.I.D. had not been to see him and was not in contact with him. We knew differently. Billy and I had talked about it with each other, we were now asking Brian to tell us exactly what he was up to. How was we going to defend ourselves at the trial if he was sneaking around and plotting things behind our backs?

I did not want to be associated with him anymore. The more he said the sicker I felt. I asked him if he had been put on any promises from the police and he couldn't speak for a moment then said he hadn't. It was written all over his face that he had been up to no good about something. He kept on going on about his uncle from St. Helens called Lenny Peters as if he was a big time Charlie, I told Brian his uncle was a gobshite, which he was and that he had a reputation of being a snitch.

I asked him was he here to fit us up like the police were trying to do. Was he going to be one of those prison specials turning up at the courts to get a lighter sentence? That means to say, he would stand up in court as a police witness and say he heard us talking about the Robbery and make us look guilty.

I could not believe it, this was devastation at the utmost. This was treachery, this bastard knew my family, he was supposed to be a friend. I could not trust him he seemed to be some one else. I looked at Billy and he said he would like to smash the life out of the snake but just stared at him with disgust. Billy frightened him, I could see that.

Brian was in such a pathetic state he actually looked as though he was going to shit himself. Billy hated him, he looked at Brian as though he were a piece of dirty rag. After leaving Brian's cell I watched to see what he would do. He left his cell like a weasel and headed for the office down the stairs. I went back to my own cell and silently screamed. What could Brian be up to? That incident distracted me from the world of prison for that morning. It was on exercise that afternoon that we were to get yet another mental blow.

A Liverpool fella approached me and Billy whilst we were on the exercise yard, he was around five foot six, built like an Easter egg with short brown hair. He had a wobbly sort of walk. He introduced himself as Joey Wooldridge. I didn't take much notice as I had Brian the snake worming around my brain.

I thought this Joey fella was just another lad from Liverpool looking for a mate, I was pre-occupied, I was not in the right frame of mind. I had no time for him. I was trying to make my excuses so he would leave me alone. He asked me when was we all up in court? I was not hearing correctly. I asked him to repeat himself, he did and he did say "we".

I stopped in mid stride and said for him to explain the "we". He said he was also charged with the Robbery! I must have went white and frozen. I must have been hit with a bolt of lightening. Was this man having a sick joke with us? He said it again and said he was serious.

There were now four of us charged with the three man Robbery! He then said he had been pointed out three times on an I.D. Parade as well! This could not be happening this was berserk, this scene was just from another planet, I could hardly breathe. Billy was standing there looking at this little fella in utter shock.

We could not speak, what was happening here? What was going on? I could not focus my head was totally wrecked, this was like something from a T.V. programme. I walked, I walked around the exercise yard in a haze. I could not think, I had a mental block. After ten minutes I was still struggling trying to grasp the reality of it all.

This now meant that all four of us had been accused of actually robbing the pub, all of us were accused of being one of the Robber's. The problem was that only three people had done the Robbery. So I tried to work it out but I couldn't. No one was accused of being a get away driver or a watch, we were all accused of doing the actual Robbery, thinking about it so was Jackie Kelly. That meant five of us had been accused of actually doing the Robbery at some stage or other. How was that possible? It wasn't.

Now as it stood in time there were four of us facing a trial that only three could face. That was it, one of us had to go! Or did they? My head went worse the more I tried to look at the scenario. I spoke to the new fella Joey and asked him about his questioning and he did not seem to have been questioned too much.

He said he was just asked basic questions about the Robbery and got put on an I.D. Parade in Southampton. Then all three victims from the pub had pointed him out, positively. I asked him how they connected him to the Robbery and he said he did not know. I asked him if he had heard of Jackie Kelly, he said no.

I asked him how he was connected to Southampton and he explained that he had friends there but his arrest was in Liverpool in an area near Anfield called Tuebrook. I was trying to extract every tiny bit of information from him to work out why the police should charge him with us three, as he must be innocent as well. Or was he?

I asked him straight if he had done the Robbery, he looked me in the eyes and I knew, I could feel the atmosphere change, he remained silent, he couldn't find an answer. The guilt was as pure as you could get from an expression. A few awkward moments passed. Before he could reply I told him to forget it, I did not want to know.

I left the exercise yard and Billy followed behind me. We were both having trouble with the situation, this was not right. We went to my cell and locked ourselves in. We had told my cellmate to go to Billy's cell and sit there till we next got opened up. We needed time to talk to each other, this was becoming a roller coaster.

Billy was the only one on the ride with me that I knew was safe. I knew he had not done the Robbery and after what we had gone through together I could not trust anyone else. We sat and contemplated the whole thing. We went into it at some length, trying to see what way this was going, I came to the conclusion that someone had to go.

The reason being that if four of us go in front of a Jury it would confuse them and put doubt in the whole case, surely the police were not that stupid, I did not under estimate them full stop. I said to Billy that it was either him to be released or myself. The more I looked at it, Billy had to be released.

He had not had one I.D positively, there was no other evidence so he was out, he had to be in my eyes. He agreed and I told him that if he was to go, would he get in touch with my solicitor. I didn't need to ask, he said he would be in the box as a witness, he wouldn't run off scared and frightened and leave me to be set up.

I felt proud of Billy, although he was not from Liverpool he was close. As close as a friend could be and this was something we would remember for the rest of our lives. He said he would shout my innocence from the rooftops. We knew the C.I.D. were really bad but, was this to be their downfall? Only time would tell.

I asked Billy what he thought of the new addition Joey, Billy wanted to rip his head off. I said it would be silly to do that, if he has done the Robbery the C.I.D. must know it and that means they must know it was not us. At the same time Joey knew who had done the Robbery, do we force him to tell or do we just say nothing for now and ignore his guilt?

It was a situation but we had up until the trial to pressure him, we did not need to rush anything. Maybe we would be set free together very soon, the C.I.D. knew it was not us so they must let us go now. Maybe not. I was annoyed that the C.I.D. were playing a big game with us and just banging people in jail innocent or not, was not the right thing to be doing. They were animals and they should be exposed. What a tangled web they have weaved.

We decided that we would just let fate take its course for now and see what was to come next, maybe they would let us all go, maybe not. Joey the new addition was sharing a cell with a skinhead. I was not sure if Joey and Brian knew each other but I would be watching. Brian's door was locked he had not gone on the exercise yard again, I didn't like it, I didn't like Brian, he could not look me in the eye.

Another day had passed by and Brian had not been seen since Joey arrived, he had gone missing. No sign or trace of him. Bed gone, him gone and nothing to give us a clue. Joey went to court and did not come back to the remand wing, he was put on the convicted wing, he had pleaded Guilty. We then got our date for the Crown Court.

# CHAPTER TWENTY FIVE
# BUILD UP TO MEETING THE
# ANIMAL AT THE WINCHESTER TRIAL

Our trial was due to be heard at Winchester Crown Court two weeks later. I spent several days on special visits with solicitor, barrister and the Q.C., whom was J.J.Rowe. He was old and very educated, he was from up North and was of great understanding. He seemed ok and I just left my life in his hands, I had no choice.

There were more bundles of paperwork for us to read that was unused by the prosecution and lots we were not allowed to have. There was so much to read through that I lay awake right through the night on some nights reading, scared in case I missed a clue. Events were moving quickly, Brian had been released and given bail mysteriously.

There were still four of us to stand trial. My Q.C. told me that he would be applying for my charge to be dismissed as in his view there was no evidence at all, he said that even if they, the prosecution, tried to say that I was pointed out on a line up, it would be laughed out of court. He said someone couldn't positively identify someone wearing or meant to be wearing a full-face balaclava. Then there was the fact that the I.D. Parade was rigged.

He had not a lot more to say. He disregarded Jackie Kelly's statement as nonsense. He wanted to know why I said she was on drugs and I told him that lots of inmates in the prison had told me. I looked forward to the trial date in February.

Jeff was still visiting me on a regular basis, he was the best friend anyone could wish for. Kenny his nephew was also a diamond, a bit daft but a real good kid. I knew his mum, she worked at Pilch Lane chip shop back in Huyton, she was a friend of my mothers. They were all good hard working people.

My mum had travelled down to see me with my sister. They were my world and I was their's. I kept on telling them not to worry about the trial as it would be thrown out. Still, I could see that they were not so optimistic, after all that had happened to me they would not believe anything until it happened.

I could see that this was still having a terrible effect on my mother she was feeling every blow I was dealt. I suppose that for a mother to witness her son go through all this devastation, would be more than enough but my mother was a fighter and she would not cave in, she just wanted to see her son home.

The visits from my mother and sister were the worst because I always had to watch them walk away and the hurt in their faces hurt me more than I could express. I did try to tell them not to visit as it would upset them so much, but it would of hurt their feelings more and I didn't want that. I wanted to see them smiling again and I could only do that when I was released from the courts.

Well February went very slow and the middle of the month eventually arrived. I had a suit and some smart shirts and a couple of ties, I looked smart and felt it. What would I do without my mother eh? Billy was looking sharp to he was also sporting a nice suit. We were ready to roll. We got on the prison bus for the five-minute drive to the Crown Court and smiled at each other, at long last we would see justice done.

We arrived in the cells at Winchester Crown Court and Joey was in the next cell. We had not been able to speak with him as much as I would have liked to, he had been moved onto another wing. I had a nickname for him now, it was Joey Bullarse. It was because of the way he wobbled along with his big arse.

He had told me from out of a window that he had thrown his hands in and pleaded Guilty because the police promised him a shorter sentence. He said he would not see us go down for it and if it come to it, he would give evidence in our favour and tell them it was not us and he could prove it. He said he would be a witness for us.

I told him to do what he thought best, it would be

nice if he told them the truth. If he was called as a witness he knew it was because we had to call him and not just for the sake of it. I felt the C.I.D. had literally got him by the balls and he would have to say who had done the Robbery with him sooner or later, if he hadn't already.

Would anyone like to be in his position if Billy or myself were to be found guilty? I wouldn't have liked to be Joey. I had asked Joey if the police had give him a hard time asking him who it was that he had done the Robbery with, he told me that was a question he was never asked. He was telling the truth as I had read his interview but I had meant "Off the record".

He told me that the only thing they had mentioned was that he would get a good result if he would indicate that I was known to him before he was captured. Which I wasn't. He told me that they were after my blood and would not be surprised at the lengths the C.I.D. would go to for a conviction against me.

I was sure he was trying to tell me something but I never got the chance to have a talk to him. It was frustrating as I knew there was something he was trying to let me know. I went to the toilet at the Crown Court and there was Joey. He told me quickly that the police wanted to see him again and he would let me know what they said as soon as he could. We were then all called into the court.

The steps leading up to the dock were the sort of

stairs that took me back a thousand years, they were stone and every footstep echoed loudly, it was horrible. I walked into the dock and was told to face the judges chair and move to the right by the warders, who were getting the instructions from De Sylva. Billy was told to stand on my left, Joey on Billy's left then Brian was brought into the dock and told to stand on Joey's left.

I looked around to see my family, I could not see, none of us could see anyone in the public gallery but we hinted our presence with a cough, as the dock was like a pigeon hole underneath the public gallery. My solicitor told me that all of my family were there and a lot of our friends had turned up for support.

There was to be a last minute change and we were to have a different Judge, it was to be the only available Red Robe Judge Lewis McCreery. My heart sank, this was the worse Judge known to mankind. He was a legend, this Judge was actually in the "Guinness Book of Records", for his sentencing mannerism. He had give more years out in one day to convicts than the whole of the Old Bailey. He was known as the animal.

He was not known as a fair Judge nor a lenient one but for being a pure bastard. I had heard so much about him and I feared him, I had seen a lot of inmates come back to the prison screaming and cursing his name. This was not good. My barrister looked over to me and told me not to worry, I wish it were as easy as that.

It was around fifteen minutes later when we were

told to rise. We all stood and in comes the man himself. He was dressed in a fine red robe and a very old looking wig, which had obviously seen a lot of trials. He must have been around sixty-five to seventy years old. He slowly viewed the surroundings of the court and made his way to the chair which was more like a throne.

He had a bundles of papers in his hands and laid them down in front of him. The rest of the court sat down but we four were told to stay put. The usher read out our names and asked if we understood the charge, then asked for our pleas. Joey was the only one to plead guilty, the rest of us pleaded not guilty. We were then told to sit down.

The Judge instructed a Jury to be sworn in. The Jury I was told by the Q.C. were to be normal average people from within the society and we would have to choose twelve from fifteen. They were shuffled in and twelve of them were sworn in. The thing about twelve men or women from normal and average backgrounds was not here.

These were twelve very well to do posh people. I could hear them when they were sworn in swearing an oath. They were not normal average people at all and every one of them was of at least university level. They were all snobs and talked very snooty. I felt I was a commoner to them. My barrister's comment of the day was that the brighter they were the better. I didn't like them, none of them.

I wanted at least some people from the lower or middle class world that I came from to be on the jury. People who knew that the police were not perfect, not these snotty looking snobs, they looked like they were from a, "butter wouldn't melt in my mouth" society. They were all the type to dine out at the local Inn and drink wine, maybe they knew the landlord? Maybe they still drank at the Ship Inn? Well my hands were tied, it was up to my legal team now.

The trial was set to start. The way the system works is that the prosecution state their case first, then the defence state theirs, then the witnesses are put in the dock by the prosecution and then the defence cross examine them.

After that the defence calls on their witnesses then they are cross-examined by the prosecution, then after all that they have a closing speech from the prosecution and defence followed by a summing up by the Judge. The Jury go out debate the case then decide a verdict, upon this they tell the Judge, then lastly you have a foreman stand to state the verdict of the jury.

# CHAPTER TWENTY SIX
## FREEDOM FOR A SNAKE
## AND LEGAL POINTS

This is how it went. The prosecution told the Judge he would offer no evidence against one of the accused and could he do that now because the defendants had made their pleas? I knew this was going to happen I had bet on it with Billy, someone had to go. The prosecution had left it a bit late I thought and I pictured Billy off out the courts free, all happy and pleased.

The Judge accepted and asked which one of the defendants did he want him to acquit. The prosecution turned and looked at all four of us, one by one starting with me. He then turned back to the judge and said he would like the Judge to acquit "Brian Peter's". The grounds being Insufficient Evidence.

I was hit with a mallet firmly on the top of the head, this was not possible. I looked at the prosecutions back and was drawn to his Junior De Sylva, grinning at me with those sneaky, snakey eyes lodged in his head. He enjoyed that moment I could see that. My head was blocked, I was in turmoil. I could not understand how they could let him go.

Without a shadow of doubt he was almost "Banged To Rights", in fact he was. There was no way he could have walked out. There was even less evidence against Joey Bullarse and he was guilty. How on earth had Brian Peters' got to walk out here, why him? This was disgusting. I wanted to scream to god almighty himself.

To actually hear the words Insufficient Evidence! I would have found him Guilty myself if I were on the Jury. I think anyone would have, it was obviously more likely to be him than Billy or myself. The whole world could see that. I did not register what happened next but somehow Brian disappeared from the dock.

The prosecution then stated that it would only be fair, if the guilty man was taken out the dock and kept at the prison until sentencing after the trial. He seemed pretty sure too, that the Jury should be discharged and another sworn in, as he would not like the defence to feel that they were prejudiced by seeing Peters' walk away.

I called to my barrister and told him that I wanted to keep the Jury. This was my defence and this Jury had seen that a man was released. When it comes out that Brian Peters' had been pointed out three times and put in custody, they would not be able to convict me on the "so called" evidence against me, knowing that there was much, much more against Brian Peters' and he had been discharged. In my thoughts it was a public admission that they had got it wrong about him yet, they continued against myself without any evidence. Thus proving they could very well be wrong about me too. The Q.C. argued the point but I could already see that Judge Lewis McCreery was all for the prosecution and the defence were not going to get much mileage out of him.

The Judge agreed totally with the prosecution. Where were the words "Fair Trial" now? This was barbaric, I felt as though the Romans were back and I was their sport for the week. I bet old Lewis up there on his throne was wearing suspenders. He seemed to be doing a bit of fiddling with something under the alter.

I looked at him with suspicion, he was not fit to be a Judge. I hated him already. He must have noticed because he stared back and growled at me, he sounded like a dog growling. I looked at Billy and then looked back at the Judge, he stopped the growl. It crossed my mind that he was reading my thoughts. He wasn't but the growl threw me into a different thought direction, he was off his head, the Judge was a nutter!

After another Jury was sworn in, the court adjourned for lunch. This Jury was worse than the first. I asked my legal team if they heard the growl? They had and told me the Judge was known in the legal system as a bit of an eccentric as most High Court Judges were. I frowned in puzzlement, this was going to be an experience indeed. I just hoped no one would let old Lewis of the leash, he would definitely bite someone.

We all went back into the court after the lunch period and the new Jury were all there and staring at Billy and myself in the dock. I wondered if they knew about Peter's or that they was the second jury? In came old Lewis delicately making his way to the throne, he could have been wearing stiletto's, he probably was as his back looked a little arched as he fumbled in, we will never know will we?

Those afternoons proceedings were all legal applications from our defence teams. The Jury were retired until the morning unless notified differently and all were sent home. I listened intently to the arguments trying to understand what they were all going on about.

I was coming to terms with the legal side of it now and grasped the fundamentals of the issues. You see they would argue what was legal evidence and what could be used in open court. It was becoming interesting and I was feeling that my legal team had more than a damned good argument.

One of the applications went in our favour, it was the confrontation identification at Southampton, that was surprising. The solicitor that represented me at the time was called to give evidence about the incident but first the Superintendent that was in charge was to give his testimony.

He stood firmly, proud and perfectly uniformed, immaculate. He said, he had asked me in person to go on an I.D Parade and I had refused. It was because of my refusal that he ordered a confrontation. It was a lie sworn under oath from the biggest, most respected policeman in Southampton. Just how sick did I feel now? Very! He was cross-examined but stuck to his story. He seemed rather good at telling lies he must have had a lot of practice.

Well next on the stand was my old solicitor, he stood in the dock very smart and sworn his oath. He was only a small man and a mild type of man but honest. He went on to tell the court how he was at the police station waiting for his client (that would be me) and was approached by the Superintendent. He said he would like to know if there would be an objection by the client to an I.D. Parade later that morning at the police station.

He said he told the Superintendent that he was sure his client would agree but, he would have to confirm it with him when he arrived at the station. He said he went on to ask his client for permission and it was agreed, he said he then conveyed the agreement in person to the Superintendent. He done it personally, so there could be no confusion.

The defence sat down and then the solicitor answered all the questions from the prosecution. He went under the cosh from the prosecuting Q.C. but stuck to his story and agreed that yes, he was calling the Superintendent a liar. That was it I thought, then I heard that growl from the judge again. Someone should have brought a muzzle.

It was now the Judges turn to have some questions. The Judge tore into the solicitor like a starving Jackal would ravish a meaty white bunny rabbit. He shouted at the solicitor, saying he was a common piece of dirt and he was not fit to be a solicitor. How dare he come into his court and accuse the Superintendent of lying under oath, in front of him!

The Judge carried on. The Superintendent was a man of extreme honour and long service. He the solicitor was a horrible little man. The Judge then told everyone on the Jury to disregard the solicitor's evidence and then turned to the poor solicitor and shouted at him, to get out of his court and never come back!

The solicitor was so embarrassed he went the colour of beetroot, he managed to mumble something out on his exit route, he said to me that he was so sorry and he would see me at the appeal courts. He knew this was going wrong, big time.

The poor solicitor only told the truth and a merciless ferocious animal attacked him. I was right I told you he needed a muzzle. The whole court was in an eerie strained silence, the prosecution then conceded that the witness from the confrontation had indicated that the descriptions were of the other person in each statement. In other words I was described as Billy and Billy as myself. So what was the point anyway I thought to myself.

The point I made from it was that this Judge in front of me was an outright vicious devil, he was beyond doubt an animal. There were no other points won and there was no throwing the case out, we were in the shit. Big shit. My only train of thought was that I would have to convince the Judge himself one way or another that I was innocent. This was a task no man on earth would relish. I broke into another sweat. Everyone in the legal teams was afraid of him including the prosecutor's.

The day concluded and I was taken with Billy back to the prison. On the bus back I asked Billy if he thought the poor little solicitor had followed through in his pants? He burst out laughing, so did the warders. The warders had to sit at either end of the dock and when we stood up they stood up, when we sat down they had sat down.

The warders broke the ice and expressed their opinions and they were of the same opinion as we were. From what they had heard and seen so far they couldn't believe that they were going through with a trial on the evidence they had listened to. It was all very nice hearing it from them but, it was the Judge and Jury that our fate depended on. We got back to the prison and had early nights, as it had been a long day. Mental exhaustion.

# CHAPTER TWENTY SEVEN
# THE ANIMALS KANGAROO COURT

The next morning we were in the dock and waiting for the first witness. It was the landlord from the pub, Roger Bannister. He told his story and I listened to his drama, it was more than an ordeal he had gone through and not one you could get over very quickly. It must, still now hurt his brain. A mental scar for life and very traumatic.

The Robbery was atrocious, it was not what I would call a Robbery. The Robber's had no style and no mercy and had no right to do what they done to him, it was disgusting. It was not like a Robbery as you would see on a T.V. programme of a bank or something. This was horrible and this really did happen.

I would call it Evil and there are different levels of sickness that people would go to for money. The week before, there were three traveller boys up in court for raiding old peoples houses in a similar way and putting pillowcases on their heads and beating them up, as old as they were. An old lady had died later from the result of her injuries.

Several of the old people Robbed were tortured but the police tracked the gang down, they all lived in Southampton. Not a mile from the Seaweed Pub that I was accused of Robbing. The three Robbers were sentenced to twelve years, nine years and seven years. Guess who sent them down? Yes you got it, good old Lewis the animal.

They had deserved sentences of that length because of what they had done, they should have got more, a lot more. They had been caught for at least three Robberies and questioned for lots more, all on old people. Now that's what I call outright evil.

My sympathy went out to the landlord, I had nothing to ask of him in cross-examination as I didn't want them to go through this, none of them. His wife was next and she gave her evidence, there were no questions for her either, except from my Q.C. He asked her to describe the balaclava, she stated it was black with just two holes for the eyes.

She also stated that there were no holes for the mouth or ears. She said about the accent of the figure with the balaclava, she was now not too sure but, one of the others had a Northern accent similar to a Liverpudlian. She was just not sure who.

She then said that at the I.D. Parade in Liverpool she had pointed out a person as Number One Robber. She was asked if anyone was in the adjoining room with them and she said a policeman but could not remember which one. My Q.C. left it at that and then out of the blue asked her where did she stay in Liverpool and with whom.

I was not expecting that one. She replied that she had stayed at the Adelphi Hotel and shared the room with her husband. She then said that they all had a drink in the bar and she with her husband retired early to bed but stressed that, she and her husband didn't stay there at the bar for to long at all. They did not feel up to it.

My Q.C. asked who "they", were and she said Graham Essary, his friend and Yvonne. My Q.C. then asked where Yvonne slept that night. She said she was not sure, she may have stayed with Graham because she didn't like to sleep alone no more. She did not recall Yvonne's bed being slept in the next morning, because she had gone in her room to see if she was having breakfast with her and her husband, she was not there.

The Q.C. was going nicely now. He asked her did she know what time Yvonne had left the bar and if so who with. She said it was late because Yvonne had called her on the hotel room phone to tell her that she was going to a club with Graham and his friend. She was then released from the stand and left the court. I felt sorry for her, she had gone through one hell of an ordeal.

I looked at the couple and could not help but think that they were old enough to be my mum and dad, it sent shivers down my spine to think that it could have been. The horror of some nutter's going through the bedroom windows was bad. I would not be advising my parents to be the landlord and landlady of a pub in a hurry. Definitely out of the question.

Next up was Yvonne Cameron, the third witness from the pub. As she was sent for the judge mumbled something, I stared at him and he was staring directly back at me, he started growling again. I thought about looking away in case I laughed with nerves but held his stare more intensely.

He suddenly stopped growling and turning to the Jury he asked aloud, what type of people were these? Then turned back and stared at both of us in the dock. I took a deep breath and blew out, slowly turning my head from side to side, this Judge was not for real. He was asking the Jury to look at us as animals in the dock.

The next witness took the stand. She went through the story of the Robbery and what she could recall. She was quite particular but all the same had suffered an ordeal. That was without a doubt. There were no questions about the Robbery at all, just about the hotel. She denied all knowledge of going to the bar, the nightclub and even denied that Esssary had stayed in the same hotel. It looked like she had something to hide.

I was pleased, as things around this copper were now looking dodgy. My Q.C. then asked how she got to Liverpool and instantly she replied that Graham had given her a...Lift. She realised what she had just said and put her head down, then was asked the golden question, had the policeman D.C. Essary told her who to pick out or shown her a photograph?

She took a minute, then said she could not remember but she did not think so. She was not sure. My Q.C. sat down, that was it she was free to go. I thought my legal team should have done more but they said to me that it merits nothing as she says nothing about me. I said I thought that the police should be exposed for what they have done, the legal team had other ideas. That was the day over.

The next morning we were all in the court room and the next few witnesses statements were read to the court, they were all of little relevance as it proved nothing and both the prosecution and the defences had all agreed to them being read. They consisted of forensic, scenes of crimes statements and hospital reports.

There were a lot of photos of the injuries sustained by Roger Bannister. They were in black and white and 'A' four in size. They were not passed to me. They had an effect as I heard the sighs from the Jury and made them look ill, then the Judge started to growl again, this was weird but, I sensed for a reason.

The Judge had waited till the Jury all had a copy then done the growling, he then repeated the same words again, what sort of people are these and stared at us. He was indicating to the Jury that we were guilty again. He should have been told to behave himself but there was no one in the courtroom with the audacity or balls to say it to him, he was swaying the Jury.

After that there was the next witness to be called, Jackie Kelly. I was pleased but sceptical. She was shown to the stand and was instructed to swear the oath. She was well dressed and looked like she could have been a solicitors clerk or something. She did not look like a low life, she was clean and tidy and looked drug free. She looked quite nice and very well groomed and elegant. Good for her I thought.

The prosecution asked her for her name, date of birth and then asked her to state what happened that dreadful night when the three Robbers had used her apartment to commit this Evil Robbery. She looked at the prosecution and said that she does not remember a dreadful night, nor did she know of three Robbers' that had used her apartment for a Robbery.

You could have heard a pin drop, the court was frozen in time. The prosecution coughed and looked at the C.I.D. and asked the Judge for a minute. Essary scrambled to the prosecution table and was full of whispers. My legal team just sat staring and observed the situation.

Essary should not have been in the court but the Judge had ruled that he could be, for legal reasons. Essary sat down at the bench next to the prosecution, a mumble was directed at the Judge and he said it would be ok for the policeman to sit with the prosecution and aid them with rest of the prosecutions evidence.

Essary was a witness and in my belief from what I had asked my legal team, he was not allowed to listen to any of the witness's sworn testimonies, or he could adapt his own evidence to suit himself and the case against me. I felt this was wrong but old Lewis the animal ran the show. He was the cock of the court. The prosecution then handed pieces of paper over and asked Jackie Kelly to read the statement she had written.

She said she had not written the statement and refused to read it. He indicated that it was her statement but she insisted it was not. The prosecution then asked the Judge to make her a hostile witness and could he read her statement to the Jury. The Judge agreed. This was now beyond anything I could have ever imagined, surely this was not legal?

Imagine if it was, any copper could say you had written a statement and then it could be read to a Jury, what chance would anyone have? The statement was read to the Jury and that was that. There was no breathing space with this Judge.

My Q.C. was first to question her. He started off by asking her why she was arrested in the first place. She told them she had been caught for fraud. He then asked her had she written the statement and she said no she had not, she had only signed a piece of paper to get out. There was then an application for the original statement to be handed over, it was.

He asked her whose the handwriting was and she pointed to Essary and said it was his. She then said he had told her that if she signs it, all the charges would be dropped. She went on to say that she had been charged also with the Robbery and because she was in such a state, she had signed the written statement handed to her by Essary. She just wanted out of the cells.

She was prompted to say if she had ever had or used drugs before and she confessed that at the time, she was a junky and Essary knew it, as he had told her which clinic to go to for help and fresh needles. He had even tried to tell her to get off the drugs, as it would get her into more trouble. I was even more gob smacked than before.

She was asked if she knew Tony Allan, she said she only ever heard of that name when Essary had told her he had done the Robbery, never had she heard or seen me before, she said she was shown a photograph of me and described it. My Q.C. looked like the cat who'd got the cream. For that second after he sat down I felt the world lifting from my shoulders. That was it, that was their case against me.

I looked at the prosecution table and saw De Sylva making a gesture toward the foreman of the Jury with his hand, whilst his Q.C. was making some sort of gesture of his own. He had his hand to his eye brow as if looking in the distance and was doing something with his other hand. I could see his shoulder move. I could smell a rat, a rat of the highest degree.

I heard that growl again and the Animal stirred in his lair then spoke. Old Lewis McCreery, the Right Honourable himself was about to say his piece. He ordered that Jackie Kelly's statement was to stand and anything she had said in this court today, was hostile and should not be relied upon. She is of no quality as she uses drugs, she must leave the court.

I could not believe my ears, he was throwing away the prosecutions live evidence yet, wanting to keep a statement written by Essary. What was the Judge playing at? He was telling the Jury not to believe her today even though she was now off drugs but, they should believe her statement, which was not even written by her and from a time when she was admittingly on drugs. Now how were we to expose the coppers behaviour?

The case was adjourned till after lunch. I was livid. I was in a living nightmare, metaphorically speaking the goal posts were moved each time I entered the goal area. My brain was so heavy, what was they doing to my head?

I saw my legal team over the break and asked them exactly what the hell was going on. My life was in their hands and everyone in the world could see what was going on. I was being framed. My Q.C. spoke to me and said that there was no evidence against me full stop and to leave it to him as he did not care what they done. No one had said I done the Robbery and all there was left was a dodgy I.D. with a balaclava.

# CHAPTER TWENTY EIGHT
## BULLIED GINGERS REVENGE

I didn't understand law to well and I could not work out what the Q.C. meant but, the junior and solicitor did. What else could I do? I had to have faith in them but I didn't. I was getting scared of it all and I couldn't do anything about it. The carry on in the court and the way the Judge was behaving was not right.

Back in court there was another application for a fresh witness to be allowed to give evidence, it was detrimental to the case, said the prosecution. The Q.C. prosecutor was waving his hands about as he spoke, he too sported an Onyx ring on his little finger. I sensed a horrible feeling that something sinister was happening around me in the court, something I could not see, he was making particular hand movements with his hands in an odd way.

What was he up to? I could not work it out. I had not seen these movements before but, I could see that there was a direction of some sort going on right here. I thought to myself that I was getting paranoid and agreed with myself that, it must be the pressure that has got me going. Everything was now suspicious, I had to watch this lot with a very careful eye. I felt in danger. I did not need my eyes testing.

The witness was allowed to give his testimony and the statements were handed to the legal teams. The excuse was that the police had only just found the man and took his the statement because he had been ill. This Robbery had happened sixteen months before. Well as usual the defence arguments were as futile as ever. The witness was called.

His name was Gary Wiltshire. He was tallish medium build and was very ginger with a side part. He was around twenty-three. His evidence was that he had been getting bullied by Billy for years and he went on to say the day after the Robbery, Billy and his mate had come into his garage and told him to hold a bag with something metal in it, a few days later they apparently came back and took the bag.

The prosecution asked him did he look into the bag and he said he did not. He said it was not tied in a knot and it was a Tesco bag rolled up into a ball. Wiltshire then went on to say it contained jewellery because he just knew it, he could tell. He was then asked if Billy or his friend was in the courtroom.

He pointed to both of us and said we were the two that came to the garage. Then he stated that Billy Willis was the stocky one and Tony Allan was the thinner one. This caused yet another debate with the defence Q.C.s.

The Judge dismissed the argument as usual.

I noticed De Sylva staring at me with a smile again so I stared right back at him and gave him a filthy look, he turned away and whispered to the Q.C. who had now sat down next to him. The prosecution Q.C. then stood and asked the Judge if he may interrupt the examination for one second. This was in the presence of the Jury.

He asked if the Right Honourable Judge would ask the defence Council for Allan, If he would ask his client (meaning me) to look to the other side whilst in the court as, his Junior De Sylva could feel the, "Evil eyes of Allan" piercing into the back of his head. It was making the prosecution team feel uneasy and they would not be able to perform their duty to the crown if Allan was to stare at them again.

After all I was accused of being an Evil Eyed Robber. I could have fell over, the cheeky bastards. What the hell was going on? My Q.C. then said he would let the client know. He turned to me and asked me not to look in the direction of the prosecution, he would talk to me about it later. This was turning into a circus. Even my own Q.C. was playing their game now.

I was around five foot ten, of thin build weighing ten stone, shaved about once every month, I was twenty one and had blue eyes. My eyes did not pop out and were not protruding or coloured black. Every one that had ever made a comment in my life about my eyes were to say they were a lovely blue or Paul Newman eyes. They were really laying this Evil Eye stint on heavy. I didn't look like a monster or behave like one and I was not very big. I was a kid. Thousands of thoughts were going through my mind.

The cross examination began, my Q.C. asked Wiltshire why he had not made this statement over a year ago, he replied that he had been in prison until lately. I thought he was sick, so the prosecution had led us all to believe. He was asked when he was released and he said a few months ago but, he hadn't made a statement because no one had asked him to.

So he was asked when was it that he was asked to make the statement and to elaborate on the surroundings of how and why. He said he was on bail for motoring offences and was arrested again yesterday for other criminal activities.

D.C. Essary had talked to him about the Robbery and told him he would help him out if he were to give evidence at the trial. That morning he was contacted by the police and was taken to see Essary at this Crown court, an hour or so ago. He had said he would give a statement and would give evidence, he did not want his garage shut down and he hated Billy Willis anyway because Billy had beat him up in a fight.

He then mentioned that he knew both the defendants very well, he said that Billy and Tony were in prison with him a few months ago. The Q.C. then asked him what prison was this, probably so he could show the Jury that it was the remand centre, Wiltshire replied and said it was at Portland Borstal. The Q.C. looked boggled, he leaned down and whispered something to Paul Garlick the Barrister, he then turned to Robert Renshaw the solicitor, then to me. Was I in Winchester and Walton for the last year and a bit? Yes I said.

The Q.C. then turned to Wiltshire and told him he was here stating a load of nonsense to a court to seek favours from the police. He said he was not but if his charges get dropped it was his good fortune for helping the police. My Q.C. said he was a spiteful little man who would do and say anything to favour himself out of trouble.

My Q.C. then turned to the Judge and aggressively told the Judge that he wanted this man struck from the proceedings because both Billy and myself were not in any Borstal. The Judge said he would only hear any applications after the next defence Q.C. had cross-examined the witness.

Up stood Billy's Q.C. with a bemused smile, give him credit he ripped Wiltshire to bits. It was obvious that Wiltshire had done a deal with the police and was there to do Billy damage and have him put away. He actually stated that Billy had bullied him for years and Billy should be locked away just for that, Wiltshire was there to inflict as much damage to Billy as possible.

I looked at Essary through the corner of my eye

and see him looking like a beacon on a lighthouse, he had been rumbled and he knew it, he was bright red, he was a dirty dog. I was sickened by what I had just witnessed. This was an evil pit I was in and it was full of snakes. Venomous, poison snakes.

Then there was the legal argument as to the witness Wiltshire, the judge decided that it would stand and that he could see no fault in the circumstances Wiltshire had made the statement under. The judge turned to the Jury and told them that maybe the two defendants were not prisoners at Portland Borstal but may have worked there. I could not believe my ears.

My ears were not hearing this, the Judge knew we couldn't have been there, it was impossible. Wiltshire had lied but the Judge didn't tell the Jury, he let the Jury think that it could have been true. This was wrong and I knew it. The Jury in my view could see right through this farce and must have been getting sick of the silly witnesses, or was it wishful thinking?

I had an outburst. I stood up and in desperation I tried to say that this was all wrong but, I almost had my head chewed off by McCreery. He screamed at me to sit down and shut up or he would try this case without me being present. I sat down quicker than I had stood up and felt the urge to use the toilet. This Judge was terrifying, make no doubt about it. My head could still hear his voice echoing menacingly around my brain. Ever felt like shouting for mummy? This was the time.

I looked at Billy and he was not saying much, there was an empty look in his face. Probably the shock of it all. I rubbed the top of my head with my hands and wished I were somewhere far away. The case was adjourned shortly after till the next day, oh boy, what a day.

On the way back to the prison Billy was very subdued, this was getting to him and even the warders were now on our side. They could not help but express their views and state what a frame up this was. They had never seen anything like the carry on they had seen this day. It was comforting to know that I was not the only one who could see it. Normal people could to. Maybe the Jury would. Who know's? I would have to wait and see.

# CHAPTER TWENTY NINE
## DETECTIVE COMMITTING PERJURY

The next day was the day that Essary and another C.I.D. were to give their evidence. Before I went in to the court I had told my legal team that I wanted them to slaughter Essary and I wanted it done with no mercy, properly. I sat in the dock as Essary was called and wondered what the next stroke to be pulled by the prosecution was.

All Essary had to say about me was that I would not speak to him. The most I had said was "no comment". I was following his testimony very carefully and even had his statement in front of me. It was the same as his statement and then he went on to talk about Billy. I had it in black and white in front of me and it was a signed statement from Essary stating Billy would not talk, would not say a word. He had just looked at the wall.

I expected Essary to say just that, he didn't. Essary claimed that when he walked into the interview room at Birkenhead police station, the first thing out of Billy's mouth was that he didn't know anything about the

Robbery on the pub in Southampton. The prosecution elaborated on it and meticulously explained to the Jury that Essary had not even told him why he was interviewing him.

That Willis knew without being told what he was about to be questioned for, in other words that he must have been guilty. This was a great cue for the Judge to put his teeth in, he spoke very loudly saying to the Jury that they must see that Willis, has practically owned up to the Robbery, then growled and said again, what type of people are these and stared intensely at us in the dock.

The Jury followed his gaze. I nudged Billy and handed him the statement to show him, I then whispered to Billy that his Legal team better do something about it, as it was in black and white in front of us. It was an act of perjury. My legal team passed the onus on to Billy's legal team, as they could not argue his case, it was up to them. They done nothing.

I said again to Billy to do something and he just froze. I snatched the statement back out of his hand and leaned over the dock and got my Q.C.s attention. The court went quiet, I said in a low and soft voice that he should ask about the I.D. and Yvonne Cameron, Jackie Kelly and everything else, also that he had just committed perjury.

He said no, and to leave it to him. The witness was now allowed to go. I felt my life slipping away and in panic I stood up and told Essary to stay there where he was and the Judge shouted at me, asking what I was doing. I didn't back down I couldn't not now. This was too serious to just let go.

I raised my voice and waved the statement of Essary, I said he had just committed perjury and this was the proof, he was a liar. Then I shouted at the defences asking why they were not doing anything about it. The Judge growled at me again and I told him he could do what he wanted with me but he should read the statement, the jury should see it. I told the whole court that Essary was a liar and he was not fit to be a C.I.D.

It was all very quiet, I had said my piece and I had nothing else to say so I sat down. The Judge broke the silence and told Essary to leave the court for a moment. He then told the Jury to go for tea. I had started something here.

They had gone now and the courtroom was full of tension. I thought he was going to throw his wig off and roll his sleeves up and beat me up but he didn't. He said slowly and menacingly to the prosecution that he hoped things were in order, as he wants no complaints from the appeal court at a later date. They assured him that all was in order.

The Judge then told the defence Q.C. of mine that he should keep me on a leash. He turned to the other Q.C. of Billy's and told him that if he had anything to say he should say it, that's what the court is for, after all it was a trial. I felt that this Judge could be coming around. I was proved wrong. He then said, who was the next witness. The prosecution asked for the other C.I.D.s statement to be read out. And the Judge agreed.

I just put my head down as this was now beyond me, I felt I had been fed to the wolfs. That was it the case was over. My Q.C. had decided that there was no need for any defence and the case was nothing. He firmly believed that there was no evidence.

The prosecution done his summing up and his basis was that I had been pointed out by the landlords wife. That was it I thought but, he then went on to tell the Jury that the other man pointed out three times on my I.D Parade had a remarkable resemblance to me! My head almost exploded, there was no case against me at all, the Q.C. was telling lies to make a case. The other bloke looked nothing like me.

The Prosecution Q.C. was making funny movements again and this time I see the pattern, what was going on here? He was making signals to the foreman of the Jury all through his speech but, the signal with the hand over the eyebrow was as if he was looking for something into the distance, it niggled away at me.

I had asked my legal team did they notice any weird hand signals and the Q.C. asked me if I was on the square? I replied of course I wasn't, I was in a circle, a vicious circle. He said that was not what he meant, I asked for an explanation and he said it was nothing to worry about. I just felt something untoward going on, in secret.

It was Wiltshire's evidence that was against Billy nothing else and that obviously should not have counted but the prosecution still continued. The prosecutor still wanted it to go to the Jury for a verdict against both of us. This was not real.

My Q.C. stood up and said that a man with a balaclava on cannot be pointed out. The S.A.S. wore them for this reason, he then quoted a point of law and said to look at the rest of the I.D. Parade and think of the person that was pointed out three times. The description was nothing like the lad in the dock.

It would be wrong to convict on that evidence alone. That was it. I could not believe he had not called up Mark the clerk to justify the dodginess of how he had viewed the I.D. Parade in Liverpool. My head was on the moon, that's all it took ten seconds, this can't be right. I felt cheated, I felt an anti climax, this was not right.

He had not even called up Joey Wooldridge to ask if I was with him, he would know he had done the Robbery. There was nothing to tell the Jury about Brian Peters either. I was baffled at it all. Billy's Q.C. was just as quick, then it was the Judge.

The Judge wanted a short adjournment to prepare his speech. We were taken to the cells. Billy was definitely subdued and did not say much. I went in to see my Q.C. where he and the rest of the legal team explained to me that the Jury could not reach a guilty verdict, it was impossible. Well they half had me believing it but I was just not sure.

I was disappointed with the way he left out all the wrong doings by the police. I went back to the cells and waited. Billy seemed much happier and was smiling, his legal team had convinced him that he was walking out. It gave me a lift and we both turned over a new feeling within ourselves. We were called up again for the Judges summing up of the trial evidence and for him to direct the Jury.

Lewis McCreery. The Red Robe Judge, began his twenty-minute speech. He explained through the Robbery and all the evidence, how he see it and basically told the Jury that the two defendants sitting in the dock, were guilty as sin. He said they would not be in the dock for nothing, then he turned and growled at us once again, longer and harder.

He then said the Robbers (took a deep breath and moved his glare in our direction), were Evil and Sadistic beings who should be locked away for a long time. He was a stark raving lunatic. This was not how I was led to believe a Judge would carry on. He had then come to the end of the speech. The Jury were sent out and we were taken to the cells to await the Verdict. Half an hour had passed and we were called back. The Jury had reached a verdict.

My Q.C. came over to the dock and said to me that he would enter a submission if I were to be found guilty, I looked at him and told him if I were to be found guilty he could take a run and jump, why should he be saying that to me? I was annoyed with his ease and mannerism and I was not happy about the way he had run the trial, there was so much proof that I was set up and statements that proved I was innocence, that had not been used.

# CHAPTER THIRTY
# THE VERDICT

The Jury were in and the foreman stood up and done a strange gesture with his hands, my head was going dizzy. He too sported an onyx ring on his left little finger. Was I missing something here? His right hand made a "cut the throat" sign using his thumb, then slowly crossed his body to his waist. It was weird. We were told to stand. The Judge asked for him to state the verdict. He stared at the prosecution and sternly said GUILTY!

The both of us had been found guilty. I was in a sort of trance I was devastated and torn to shreds inside. I stood standing while the Judge rambled on to my Q.C. that he should make submissions, I could hear him telling the Judge that he was sacked and would take no further part in this unsavoury court, he was now having a pop at the Judge for real.

My mind was numb and I could not focus, everything was echoing in my head, I was taken down and taken back to the prison. I was told somewhere along the line that I was to be sentenced the next morning but I was oblivious to everything and every one. I could not speak and all I could hear was echoing of voices in my head.

I awoke after an hours sleep the next morning and was told to get ready for court, I did and felt that I was in someone else's body, as if I had risen from the body I was in. I felt as though I was looking down at myself from above. I was numb. Was I on the way to the gallows to be hanged by the neck?

I went to the court in silence and was asked by the barrister if the Q.C. J.J.Rowe could still represent me, I shook my head and walked away. I was guilty of nothing I was innocent, what had these people done to me, I couldn't speak I had a mental blockage and felt numb. They could not hurt me anymore, not with anything.

I didn't give a toss what sentence they hit me with I didn't care, what would it matter. I was innocent and it was wrong. I was taken up the stairs with Billy and the court room was in silence, I looked around and felt an enormous hatred come over me for the people in there. I couldn't even pity this bunch of self-righteous pompous bastards.

I looked up at the Judge and to my amazement, there sat a lady to his right. He looked like a pre historic gargoyle of some sort but the thing sitting next to him looked even more ancient. There was an old woman dressed in a Victorian outfit, with a big fancy ugly looking feather in her hat, sitting there to his right.

She must have been at least in her nineties, it was as if she had been dug up for the occasion. What the hell was she doing there I didn't know. Was it his wife on a day out? She would not have been out of place at a table feast with King Henry himself, the clothing she had on was something not from this century, they were medieval or something.

There was an uncanny eerie atmosphere that I could feel but the numbness in my brain was still there. Was I about to be hanged? They then brought in Joey Wooldridge and a warder stood between him and Billy, there seemed to be extra warders today. I stood erect, straight backed and head up, as if in a firing line and uttered to the Judge, do what you want you cannot hurt me now, as I was already brain dead.

He tried, I had been sentenced to twelve years imprisonment. I saw the jubilance on Essary's face as I turned to look at him and said in a loud voice that, it will all come out, it will all come out in the end. I couldn't hear anything else as I was taken down to the cell alone, frog marched by two warders' that seemed to be in a hurry for their tea.

Five minutes later Billy was brought in to the cell, he had received eleven years. We were both called for a family visit through a big thick glass screen for five minutes. I stood and looked at my father and two brothers. They were going mad, they told me to be strong it was not over yet, that we would win the appeal. I was numb but managed to ask where my mother was?

They told me she had not took it too well, I felt a tear coming into my eye, the lump in my throat getting bigger, I felt I had let them all down and caused them this heart ache, I could see it in all their eyes, this would kill my mother.

The warder's coughed, hinting the time. I said I had to go and to all look after my mum, I couldn't let them see me break. I walked away. I went back to the cell and stared into space.

I was traumatised and felt no urge to even breathe. I was dead, I wasn't me anymore I was not alive, I was the walking dead. I was a human zombie, I had nothing left inside me at that moment in time. Nothing at all. I felt a tear coming down my face, I wiped it away and refused to cry, I could not let these people break me. I had to be strong, I had to become a man there and then.

## Sadistic gang's victim lashes out at his attackers:

# 'SHOOT THESE SCUM!'

**A SOUTHAMPTON publican, whose family was robbed by a sadistic gang who threatened to pour petrol over them, today said: "They should be shot."**

Ron Bannister lashed out on the merciless trio who were jailed for a total of 31 years at Winchester Crown Court.

"They should be blown off this earth. Just got rid of. Taken out to the wastelands and shot.

"We don't want scum like them in society. We want it cleaned up, and the quicker someone does it, the better."

Mr Bannister, tenant of the Seaweed public house in Weston, made his acid remarks after a judge had jailed Joseph Allan, 23, of no fixed abode, for 12 years; William Willis, 23, of Meggeson Avenue, Townhill Park, Southampton, for 11 years; and Joseph Woolrich, 24, from Liver-

REPORT from
JOHN HOSKINS

pool, for eight years, for the night-time raid on the pub.

Though the terrifying incident happened almost 15 months ago, the nightmare is still going on for Mr Bannister, 46, his wife, Sara, their four-year-old son, George, and the then live-in barmaid Yvonne Cameron.

The anguish caused by the raid is partly responsible for their decision to quit the pub and head for a new life in Somerset.

"We have been increasingly disenchanted by the trade and I hope by moving to a cottage in the West Country we can put some of the trauma of that night behind us."

The landlord said they would however never to-

tally forget the terror of that night when the evil trio burst into the pub and stole £8,300.

"How can anyone forget the terrifying experience of someone pouring gin over your body, making it out to be petrol, and threatening to set it alight? We have all been badly affected.

■ TURN TO PAGE 3.

VICTIM: Ron Bannister after the attack.

JUICE RATE RISE ON WAY

and I want to go on non-day for the first time

Amanda Owton, 21, dents had been going on added.

two nurses from hun-

# 'SHOOT THE SCUM'

**FROM FRONT PAGE.**

"What we went through I would not wish even on my worst enemy. The experience was that bad."

Mr Bannister has been badly affected. He now suffers from chronic depression after being beaten over the head with a stick and is still receiving medical treatment.

Unlike his wife, he can no longer sleep and the pub's flights are kept on all night. "Once I slept like magic for eight hours. Now it's nothing

for me to sit up all night, be downstairs at 3am and be waiting for someone to come crashing through the windows and god help anyone who did."

He said his son now had to sleep with them in bed. "George is very well collected but he no longer will go into his room at night to collect his quilt or get some toys. From the word go, he used to sleep on his own. Now he has to go to sleep with us."

THE SEAWEED INN

ANGRY: Mr Bannister pictured today with his wife Sara (left) and Yvonne Cameron.

# CHAPTER THIRTY ONE
## HIGH RISK CATEGORY "A"

We were taken back to Winchester prison and I was put straight into a single cell. I was put on the convicted wing and I lay on the bed not wanting to move. I looked at my radio, it was a Roberts Rambler, Tracey had bought it for me, I thought of her for a while and I would not see her till I was in my thirties now.

I switched the radio on to try and occupy my mind with some music only to hear the news on the local station, it continued to rub the salt in my wounds. "Man with Evil Eyes sentenced to twelve years imprisonment, Second man Eleven years and a Third man eight years." So Joey had received eight years then.

The most hurtful thing I heard was the reaction from the landlord of the pub. He was quoted on the news as saying that, the people convicted of the robbery, should be taken to the woods and bound to a big tree and shot. Blasted to hell.

A thought crossed my mind about him and I wondered if he had contemplated that the convicted robber's might have been innocent. If the thought had of crossed his mind would he have said that in public? The news had quoted me as threatening the court from the dock as I was given the sentence.

They said that I had shouted that I would get out and that I would get them all back. Twisted bastards, I had only said that it would all come out in the end. Nothing sinister like they quoted. The whole world seemed to be taking liberties with me in public.

I switched the radio off, I was sick of hearing my name on it. I couldn't sleep my mind was running wild. The sentence did not bother me, they could have given me twelve months or twenty-five years, it was the conviction, that's what really hurt, being brandished as Evil and Sadistic. I was not that person.

I thought about it all night and I come to a conclusion there and then, if I am to be kept in prison I will stay in for something I had done. Simple. This had changed me and very shortly I would snap out of the shock of it all.

The whole trial and the events raced through my mind, I was not going to let this go. I had been forced into this situation and I was going to fight an appeal, I was also going to do the time waiting for the appeal my way, not by their rules though, no, things have changed so I will change as well and adapt to the surroundings.

I will show these people, I will put my fingers up to the system. I pictured Bennet the copper from Liverpool who questioned me for the shooting and thought to myself that he and Essary were responsible for my fate. I wanted to go into their dreams and give them nightmares about what they had done to me. I awoke the next day and I didn't leave the cell, I couldn't be bothered I was having a strange sleeping pattern.

The second day I felt I was ready to face the world. The door opened and out I went but all the other prisoners were still locked in. This was very strange, I spotted Billy and asked him what was going on, he told me to look outside my door. There was a piece of card hanging on the light switch with the letter "A". I was now Category "A".

Another kick in the teeth, this meant that we were now classed as very dangerous prisoners and as such had to be kept with other very bad prisoners, there was five of us on the wing. There was also a few more on another wing.

They were all proper nutter's, all in for Murder and I was very weary. One of them was a real sicko, his name was Danny Mudd, he had killed before and after Five years at Broadmoor was released and killed again. This time it was a woman and there was some very nasty rumour's flying around about what he had done with her.

A few days later I was called on a solicitors visit, it was Paul Garlick to discuss the appeal, he would know a date within three months. I had learned by now that the legal process is a long one in general but rather fast when it suited them. He explained that we would get leave to appeal and I would have a new Q.C.

I went back to my cell and waited for dinner. I saw Billy and he told me he had walloped Mudd in the showers. He had broken his nose after Mudd had tried to dictate his authority. I told Billy not to forget it, as he was an official psychopath doing life and had nothing to lose. We both had to tread carefully as we were the only ones not doing a life sentence for murder.

There was no more trouble from Mudd and a couple of weeks later he was gone to a nut house again. It was around six weeks later when we were both taken off Category "A". It was a relief. I didn't know until then that we were to wait at Winchester for the appeal date then we would be sent to other prisons. Dispersal prisons they were called they contained long termers and lifers only. I was only twenty-one, so was Billy. We were too young for this.

The warders asked me which Dispersal prison I would like to go and I laughed. I told him to send me wherever he wanted, as I would not be staying. I would be going home on appeal. I was getting an attitude now and I really didn't give a shit no more, it was all making me turn nasty.

I was going down for my dinner and there was only Cheese this or Cheese that, I told the head chef that I was allergic, the Doctor had noted it and said I would be able to have something else. The chef said there wasn't anything else and told me to move along.

He smirked and nudged the person next to him to show his authority, I felt he was provoking me and every body could see. I picked a tray up with something else on and he said to me it belonged to someone else on a Muslim diet. I said if I don't take it I would be without food. He said again that I could not have it and tried to snatch the tray from me, I pulled back and told him that if I couldn't have it then neither could he. Why should I starve?

He looked me up and down and called me an " Evil Eyed " little bastard. That was the last words he spoke for a couple of months. I cracked the fat prick across the face with the back of the tray and punched his head all over the hot plate. That will teach him a lesson speaking down to people.

I was pulled off by other warders and dragged off to the solitary block kicking out and screaming obscenities at them. They give me a bit of a whacking and put me in solitary for a month. I didn't care. It came to light while I was in solitary that most of the warders from the prison drank in their regular together, The Ship Inn.

That was all I needed, it was the landlord from the Seaweeds old pub. I was popular and now I knew why. I didn't really care any more, I had lost the type of person I was, I had now become different, in a lot ways. I had got used to the abuse that some of the warders would shout through the locked door about how bad I was and being from Liverpool. I just put my finger up every time a remark was made about the area I was brought up in.

I was always one to get on with things and used to being a hard worker. I trusted most people and was a happy go lucky sort of person who never took anything for granted and loved to have a laugh. This had all changed me and I was always filled with a hatred and distrust. I would not think twice about lashing out. It was not me, It was almost as if I was punishing myself and any one who got in the way. I was angry with the world.

I was shipped out to Exeter Prison and put straight in the block. I got there by transit van in a body suit. I had been sitting in the cell at Winchester over the dinner hour when a lot of warders burst in and tied me up in a sort of rubber thing with lots of strings. I was carried to a van placed in the back on the floor and several warders took great delight in sitting on top of me to ensure I did not move, the whole way.

# CHAPTER THIRTY TWO
# WELCOME TO MY WORLD

Around an hour and a half later I was carried to a cell. It took three days for me to find out I was in Exeter Prison, in solitary. I could shout to Billy, as he was pretty close by. The cell I was in was without light except for a bulb. They had blocked the view and natural light by building a brick wall in the window frame behind the bars.

I spent Twenty-Eight days in solitary. I read Lord of the Rings and it took me out of my world for three days. There was a stupid Governor that came to my cell every morning and antagonised me. He would be sarcastic and ask me how it was in my world with a silly smile on his face, the warders used to tell me to ignore him so I did, well I tried.

Billy and I were moved back to Winchester after our "Lay Down", that was the official term used for sending the naughty boys away. We had been accused of instigating a riot. It was true, the place needed a refurbishment and proper management so I was quite happy to demolish the place but, it didn't quite happen.

I had intended to lead the riot from my wing and take to the roof to protest my innocence. You see that day I had a letter telling me that my appeal had been refused. I was not going to be lost in the Prison system and forgotten. Now here I was back again after a month in the darkest corner of the Country, so I thought.

After a short time I had a solicitors visit, it was Paul Garlick the Barrister. He told me he had taken the initiative and re-applied for a hearing since the appeal was refused, I would know within a few months. I thought, at least he was fighting and told me over and over that he knew that I was innocent. I felt he knew more than he was letting on.

Another few months went by and I was off for another "Lay Down" back to old sunny Devon, Exeter prison again. I had caused more trouble within the prison that had not gone down too well, a sex offender was found to have suspiciously fallen over and tripped down the stairs. He suffered multiple head wounds. What a shame.

I was back in the dark solitary cell as before at Exeter and this time only for twenty-one days. I didn't really give a toss. I was immune to anything they did to me. I was put on the landing with all the other inmates and found it difficult. They were not letting me go back to Winchester for some un-explainable reasons. There was not one person doing any longer than eighteen months, I felt very different.

One day I was lying in bed and a warder came in and told me I had to go to work, I explained that I did not work, I was pending appeal and until then I would not work as I was innocent. I think he was deaf because he came back to the cell and told me to go to work again, five times that morning.

He pissed me off, so I said I would show him what I meant by not working as he didn't understand what I was trying to tell him. I went into the workshop and smashed all the machines and furniture up, I went back up to the same warder and told him that now because he was deaf, no one could work. Another twenty-one days in solitary. I used to blank the world out and just cut myself off mentally and nothing could effect me, it's a sort of yoga thing but not yoga.

It was my way of meditating and letting time pass by, I was taught it when I was a little kid, it was a Maori thing, if you didn't want to be there in mind you didn't have to be. I could sort of step out of myself and not have to experience or feel the surroundings. It was a good tactic that helped me not to go insane, I was proud of my ancestral Maori blood. My family were half Kiwi and the elders from New Zealand.

Well, the silly Governor continued to antagonise me with his cruel words of, how was it in my world? He took pleasure in saying it and began to incite a nasty streak that was developing in me. After another refusal to work and many nights in solitary I decided to let him know just how it was, in my little world.

The door opened and his Chief of staff greeted me with a warm good morning. He then said the Governor was here to see me as usual, the Governor asked me how it was in my little world again. I looked at the Chief and he rolled his eyes back in disappointment at the governor and turned away. He knew the Governor was pushing me once again.

I beckoned the Governor to come closer, he undone his blazer ready to fight and like a prise idiot stepped closer. I give him a swift punch to the side of the jaw, it caught him a treat and he collapsed, like a bag of shit on the floor trying to crawl out of the door to safety. He was trying to shout for help but the Chief stayed put with his back to the incident, he knew the govenor had asked for it.

"Welcome to my world". I said and the Chief turned and put his hands up saying, no more he has had enough. That will teach him to take the piss I told the Chief, he said he knew and dragged him out locking the door behind him.

I recieved an extra Eighteen months for that but I did not care. I was eventually let back on the normal wing where a particular warder took a shine to me. He was a gym instructor as well and worked out each day.

He had worked in dispersal prisons for twenty years and was still in the service for another fifteen so, basically he was a lifer who just went home at night. He was fit as a fiddle, he seemed ok though and put me right about prison and prison politics.

I spent most of my time in the gym doing circuit training and playing football. It occupied my mind, I loved football anyway but it was all I had left. I would lose myself and play with a passion and I was good at it. I was from a different world compared to most of the people in this prison, my next-door neighbour for instance, was in for Rustling. Yes! Sheep rustling! They were not bad people just different people and different ways of life. To them I was from the big city and on a big sentence.

I was called into the office and told they had a place for me in the dispersal system, it was at a prison called Parkhurst, On the Isle of Wight. I would be there within a week. I was happy to be on my way but what about my appeal? I was under the impression that I was to go for appeal before I got sent to the long termers prison. There was nothing at all happening at the moment concerning the appeal and I had heard nothing.

All of a sudden the whole prison was moving out of my way, even the warders were standing aside to let me pass. It seemed something was strange, then an old warder called me over and said to me that the last prisoner they had go to Parkhurst from that prison was back in the sixties and he was the Mad Axe Man, who had something to do with the Kray's.

I told him not to worry there will be lots more, I

was not the first and I would not be the last and I was not a big time Charlie Potato. He did not seem convinced and it seemed to me that the whole prison was looking at me like I had six heads.

It was strange, even the warder that had got me into the gym wanted to have a little chat with me, he seemed to give me good advice as he had worked there. He told me to not say a lot, keep fit and don't get involved with the politics within prison. I took that advice and it steered me well in the right direction.

# CHAPTER THIRTY THREE
# INNOCENCE OF I.R.A. BOMBERS

My trip to Parkhurst meant I would stay a few days in Winchester enroute. This was not to be a good one. I was not welcomed at Winchester and they made it clear in the reception area. I was told that there was no room on the wings and I would have to go in the solitary unit for a few nights because of the lack of space.

This I did not believe and the inmates that worked there in reception told me so, I was getting a hard time and all I was doing was passing through. Well one thing led to another and I ended up fighting a losing battle, quite a few warders jumped me and I let off very few punches. They done me again and I ended up on the floor in solitary with a big fat pig sitting on top of me, then he done a runner for the door and slammed it shut behind him.

I didn't care they could not harm me so I kicked the door and shouted obscenities non-stop, until I had my personal belongings. I was in a solitary cell within a solitary unit, known as the I.R.A. block, very secure. They came with my personal things eventually and I sorted through them. I could not find my radio so I pressed the bell non-stop.

The door opened and they flung a bag through the door. It crashed to the floor with a metallic clang, I opened it up and there it was, my radio, all smashed to bits. It was obvious that they had jumped all over it, it was now irrepairable. I see black, I see red and I went off my fucking head. I went berserk.

The radio was special to me and was the one thing I would take comfort in and of course it reminded me of Tracey, they were playing with my emotions now, they were sick. The warders were nothing short of despicable emotionless bastards.

I picked up the metal bed and hauled it at the door and tried to cave the door in. I bashed the door left right and centre, I smashed it every way I could. The bed was now a bit mangled and twisted to strange angles, I then decided to stand it up and set an ambush for when the warders come, to calm me down with their batons.

They did not come, the closest they come was to the door entrance of the block, where they taunted me with silly names and strange noises. I promised them that when I was opened up I would grab the first one in sight and smash him up. I told them I was innocent, it would be proved and then I would walk away free for anything I done wrong whilst in their custody because, I should not have been in there to start with.

I heard some-one shouting, telling me to shut up

and stop making a noise, I told him to shut his mouth I was innocent and I would fuck him up if he wanted some. I heard the voice again and the voice was telling me that I was getting nowhere and all I was doing was giving the warders pleasure and something to amuse themselves with.

I asked the voice what he meant and he tried to explain that I was their amusement for the night, that I should just channel my energies into reading a book or something. I told him to fuck off, I was innocent and would not be kept quiet for anyone. To my amazement he told me in a nice manner that he understood and asked my age and what I was in for and how long.

I told the voice I was twenty-one and what had happened to me. He was surprised that I was only twenty one, I asked him how could he understand, who was he to preach to me, as you could only understand if it happened to you. He said he knew and that he had been screaming for fifteen years that he to was innocent, since he was twenty one, I told him to behave he was having me on.

He asked if I had heard of Paul Hill or the Guilford Four? I said I had not and who the hell were they? He said it didn't matter I would be too young to know. I was curious as to why he mentioned it, I pressed for answers and he explained to me that the Guilford Four were set up by the police and imprisoned for I.R.A. bombings on pubs in Guildford. A lot of people died and were mutilated. He was one of the Guilford four, he was Paul Hill, he had been convicted of it.

I had never heard of them or his name, I remembered when I was a kid that there was always bombings by the I.R.A. on the news on T.V. I asked him how come he was still in prison, what happened to his appeal? He told me they had been used as scapegoats and the longer I am in prison and moving about I would meet even more innocent people and would hear more disturbing stories of how the system worked.

What he told me gave me the shiver's, the system seemed to be able to engulf a person and hold him down for decades. This was frightening if he was telling me the truth. I thought about it and I come to the opinion that he was pulling my leg, I would have a word with this fella on the exercise yard.

I was told the next day that I would be gone within twenty-four hours. I went to the cell next door to have a look at this Paul Hill fella. I pulled the spy hole back and see a tall thin fella with long hippy like hair with thin features sitting at a chair. I said hello and told him I was from next door, he smiled and came over to the door and said a few words.

He seemed to be truthful, he had been through some shit I could see it in his eyes. He was concerned that I should take his advice and seek out a friend of his when I got to Parkhurst, his name was Bob Maynard. He would be the one that would help me in my fight for freedom, he would guide me, all I had to do was ask for Bob and tell him that Paul said I should seek his guidance. As he knew the ropes.

He apparently knew what the system was all about and would stop me going down the wrong roads. I told Paul I did not appeal against the sentence I didn't care about that, I just wanted the conviction over turned.

Paul Hill was the first prisoner I met that had the time to try and put my head straight, understood where I was coming from and accepted my actions.

I was moved out later that day and I went to his cell and said my farewell to him. He smiled and wished me luck, I in return wished him all the best and hoped he would get justice if he was innocent. I still did not trust anyone's word, I did not think I ever would again.

Well, I was on my way to Parkhurst and it was a lovely day nice and sunny. I was taken handcuffed to two warders either side of me in a transit van with windows. I was taken to the Isle Of Wight ferry terminal at Portsmouth and we boarded straight away, after all the warders had a convict to deliver, they had a priority.

Once the ferry was on the move the warders handcuffed both my hands to the built in bars and stepped outside the van, they mentioned that if the ferry was to sink I would be going with it.

# CHAPTER THIRTY FOUR
## PARKHURST UNIVERSITY OF CRIME

I was so relieved to get to the other side in one piece. I was in Parkhurst reception within minutes. I was processed through the system as usual and taken to "M" wing. I was taken into the office and told the regulations and the rules of the prison. It was all a lot different to the previous prisons and seemed to be more relaxed, it was as if the convicts were in charge.

We could cook food in a kitchen and we could do lots of gym. We were also allowed a small allowance each week from our private and personal cash. This seemed ok. The warders were so different and called me by my first name, this I found uncomfortable to start with. I felt that I was not in a prison but a sort of unit of some kind.

I made my way to my cell and was stopped by a big tall cockney with ginger hair, he was polite and asked where I was from and how long I was doing, then mentioned that I would be ok in there. He said he had seen the television coverage of the case. It was on the local T.V. and he had seen it.

He shook my hand and made me feel welcome, his name was Steve Davies, I giggled as I thought he was having me on about the famous snooker player but it really was his name. He was alright I liked him. I see him later on and he wised me up on a few things, to steer me in the right directions.

I was green and still wet behind the ears at this level of prison life. So my mind was open to as much knowledge as possible. I unloaded my personal things into my new cell and I was even allowed to wear some of my own clothes so it did not feel to bad, the novelty of it all amused me.

After unpacking I stood outside the cell looking over the landing and observed the atmosphere, it was a very strange one. A bloke came up beside me and introduced himself to me, Mickey Fagan, he was doing ten years for a security van robbery.

He asked if I had any paperwork to do with my case and I said yes, I had bundles of them, he told me to always keep them handy as the warders would slip sex offenders on to the wing all the time and if you didn't have your paperwork some of the convicts would get suspicious. This was a good idea I thought, everyone should have their paperwork handy.

After my second day a big fella came to my cell and introduced himself as Kerry, he said because every one in the prison was from London and no one knew me it was making some of them wonder what I was in for, I smiled and showed him my paperwork He read a couple of bundles of my papers and asked for a cigarette then, another cigarette and then apologised to me, for checking me out as I was safe.

I smiled and said no problem and now that it was established that I was ok, he should now show me his proof. He looked at me in disbelief, he said everyone knew him and there was no need for him to show his paperwork. I told him I didn't know him from Adam, so for my piece of mind he should now prove himself to me, fair is fair.

How dare this cheeky big fucker come up to my cell as if he was the Governor? My neighbour Mickey was in the middle and calmed the situation down in a tactful manner. I didn't care how big this Kerry was, I would pick something up and hospitalise him, he was a prick and he wasn't going to get away with it on me. He seemed sly and slippery, I took an instant dislike to him straight away.

He left the landing and went off, he had ruffled my feathers but also enlightened me on a couple of facts. To be on this "M" wing, you had to be rather clever at manipulating things like riots or had to be some sort of threat to the system, it was a small wing and that was so we could be watched carefully.

Mickey told me that Kerry was from Kent and not to worry as he (Mickey) had a lot of friends in there, I would be looked after and Kerry was not really liked.

So I listened to all he could tell me and absorbed all the advice he had to offer over the next few months. He was in his early fifties and knew quite a lot, he introduced me to quite a few of his pals.

They were all in for very long times and were all in for armed robberies. Most of them were nice ordinary fellas, each one of them was intelligent and knew everything there was to know about crime. In fact every one of them was almost famous, they were all headliners and top of their game no matter what it was. This to me was like a Criminal University.

I had no choice in the matter I was sent here and basically thrown in at the deep end with the biggest villains in the country. I had so much to absorb and this was interesting, I wanted a degree in criminology, I wanted to know everyone's story and how they were caught or how others had got away with things. What else could I do?

I was advised to go on to education lessons in the prison and get some proper certificates so I did. I was educated at Prescot Grammar School just outside Liverpool so I was not thick and I soon attained several A levels in mathematics, Geography and English.

I learned how to play Back Gammon and played for hours with a bloke called Ray Baron, it soothed the mind, he was the one with a brain, he had attained himself a degree and I liked him, everyone did. He was very intelligent.

I was asked if I would like to work in the kitchen and after discussing the benefits with Mickey, I accepted the offer. I found that to be working there put me in a good position, I could have lots of meat away and other little perks. One of the perks was to pass notes on to the S.S.B. This was the special security prison wing. Good tips.

It was under huge security for the huge villains. My perk was to pass on messages to and fro from the main wing to the S.S.B. I felt that I was now trusted from the highest status and it pleased me. I had a role to play and it was respected. The job only lasted six weeks, I had an argument with some idiot and the Chef decided that the incident was a dangerous one and could possibly lead to a fatal stabbing again. As a few months before, someone used a knife and stabbed a fellow inmate to death. So I had to go from the kitchens.

I stayed in the gym and spent almost six hours a day training, I was getting very fit and much stronger. I had received a letter to state that my appeal had now been passed and would be heard in the near future. I was asked by one of the inmates if I would like to go to Long Lartin Prison as his brother was in there and wanted a transfer to Parkhurst.

He said if I did, I could just tell the office and they would arrange it. I thought about it and looked at the benefits of the move, it would be easier for me as the prison was up north and Billy was there. It would be easier for visits to, it was too far at Parkhurst for my family to come, all the way to the Isle of Wight, although I was ok.

It would be nice to show my mother that I was doing well, getting bigger and looking healthy. I decided to go for it, I was told it had a proper football pitch and that there was lots of football with a giant gym and the rules were as good as the ones here in Parkhurst. The swap was on, that's if it was ok with the warders.

I went in and asked for a transfer and mentioned the other inmate at Long Lartin, they said they would get back to me. The next day I was told that I would be transferred a week later. That's how Parkhurst was, a proper prison where you could get on and get time done, to me everyday was another day closer to my appeal.

I was due a visit before I left and I see Jeff as usual, he was as loyal as they come and never failed not to turn up. He loved coming up to the prison as everyone that got a visit was a someone and Jeff had read all about them in the Sunday papers and the Daily ones.

He was star struck and I would have to spend most of the visit explaining who was who and then he would be happy. Most people had hit the headlines, some from the Brinks Mat Robbery, the Chain Saw gang, the list could go on and on. Jeff asked how the hell I could feel safe with all these villains and I explained that, they were no different to anyone else except they had done a bigger crime and hit the head lines.

They were no different to normal workers except their work was illegal. I personally had to survive here and could not and didn't want to see no difference with them. I explained to Jeff that at the end of the day, we were all living in the same big house and under the same roof and basically had to fit in with each other. We all detested sex offenders and informers, that went right across the board.

I knew that the occupants of the big house were having an effect on me and obviously my surroundings were rubbing off on me. He smiled and agreed but he couldn't help saying that he looked forward to seeing the Sunday papers every week, so he could see who he was likely to bump into on a visit. He was loving it.

He was good company and made sure that I got a visit every time I was due one and I respected that. He cheered me up with the news from home and told me what I was missing on the outside. He was still working hard and had now got a house and was renting his flat out, I used to tell him to get into the Daily Times and do the stocks and shares.

He didn't because he couldn't read that well, too many big words and the Times he said would take a whole day to read. I used to read the Times paper every morning then I would read the Guardian. It gave me the latest knowledge on all the stock exchanges and kept me up to date with all the recent changes in the law.

I was like a walking information pack. I was learning and maturing mentally into a dictionary of crime. Jeff encouraged me to keep learning and not to waste the time in prison, I agreed that I was just as well getting something out of it, than nothing at all. I was trying to fill my mind up and not dwell on the appeal.

# CHAPTER THIRTY FIVE
# LONG LARTIN AND ITS CLIENTEL

I was off to Long Lartin prison it was situated in Evesham, Worcestershire. Just south of Birmingham. I had been given almost a sack full of notes to pass on to the inmates of Long Lartin from their friends and brothers at Parkhurst, I was the grape vine. I was given a good send off and a lot of them shook my hands and wished me farewell.

The only person I did not see was Bob Maynard, he had been shipped out and ghosted to another prison just as I had arrived at Parkhurst. Maybe he would be at the next prison. I left the prison with a warm smile, as the occupants had all helped in a way to bring me up and condition my brain, they had also put me in a position to determine what was right from wrong, in the moral department. I was now twenty-two and not so green.

On my transfer I was taken to another prison and we picked up another convict on his way there, I was hand cuffed to him on the way. He was a few years older and was asking me all about the prison and I told him what I had heard of it.

His name was McCarthy from Staines, he was doing ten years for Armed Robbery. I gave him the best advice as I could and he appreciated it, here was me giving advice to older convicts. I felt so different now. Long Lartin looked massive from the outside. I went through reception and was processed just like before.

I was taken to D wing, the set out was quite different and there was a lot more convicts on the landings. The doors were all electronic just like an American style prison. There was also an intercom type of thing on the wall, I didn't like that and was to look at it with suspicion every day there after.

While at another prison earlier on during my stay I had made friends with a good lad from Southampton called Jimmy Bennett, he got in some trouble with a gang of Welsh fellas and he had to fight one of them. Well he battered this Welsh fella and left him in a terrible state, I was the only witness and I had received six weeks solitary for not writing a statement against him, I heard no evil saw no evil and didn't speak no evil.

That's the way prison worked and to co-operate with the system will set you up in a vicious circle that was not worth living in, informers are a bad breed in the system and get hurt, seriously hurt. He said he owed me one and would repay me one day.

My new neighbour to my right was called Jimmy Bennett also, he was serving Twenty-Five years for

Bombings, for the I.R.A. On my left was his mate Jerry also doing Twenty-Five years for I.R.A. Bombings. It just so happened that my mate from Winchester Prison who was from Southampton was my neighbour, Jimmy Bennett's nephew.

He already knew who I was and introduced himself, he was a small man and told me his nephew spoke well of me. I was glad I was not the taffy that tried to get his nephew six years. Also there were two Liverpool lads, one was called Caddy, I had met him in Winchester he was doing a Six year sentence for a Robbery and John Hasse, he was doing a fourteen year sentence for Armed Robbery. He became a proper friend. His co-accused was from Huyton, Danny Vaughn, I had heard of his family back in Liverpool.

Opposite my cell was a nutter from the Middle East called Fahd, a friend of Gadaffi, he was a very funny fella always having a joke. Next to him was Bob Knapp another Armed Robber from London. There was also Hughie Callaghan, he was not a terrorist but was fitted up and framed for the Birmingham Bombings, he was innocent and was getting old and he had spent almost fifteen years in prison so far fighting for his Liberty. It was outrageous. Hughie and his co-accused were known in the system as the Birmingham Six.

The next day I went on to the field for exercise, I could practically walk anywhere in the prison that I wanted to there was so much freedom. It was like a village within four walls, it was like being let loose. The football pitch was fantastic and I was desperate to play in a game. This was going to be a good place to stay while I waited for my appeal.

There had just been a roof top protest by another inmate called Vinney Hickey. He was shouting for his liberty also, he had been convicted of the Carl Bridgewater Murder and sworn to the almighty from the rooftop that he was innocent. He was, someone else had done the Murder and every one knew it but the Appeal Courts would not over turn his conviction.

His brother Michael had been sectioned under the mental health act, in other words they had nutted him off, the poor bastard was totally innocent.

I had learned that it was so easy to frame and set up someone to gain a conviction but, so much more impossible to put it right, the system seemed not to want the Public Embarrassment of saying their system sometimes got it wrong.

It made me feel sick to think I could be fighting a loosing battle. As time went by it felt even more sickening, thinking that they had forgotten me. There was a lot more people than myself who had been dealt bad blows and were living on nothing but hope. I had to pull my finger out and be counted, I knew that much and had to do whatever it took to make sure I was heard loud and clear.

I had to have a good chat with Billy and see how

he had faired over the last year. I had not seen him but I was glad to see him now and see how he was coping with the situation. I linked up with him and we chatted in depth for quite a while.

I got the impression that Billy had almost given up. He had no faith in the appeal. I didn't blame him but I was not going to sit back and let it go without some sort of battle, I would think of something and we should do it together, our own protest. He was a bit sceptical but I thought I would talk him around later on.

He was not in the right frame of mind and I told him that being surrounded by all these injustices were not helping him, to see all these innocent people must have stung his brain. I could see with just looking around that in our position, you are forced to see no light at the end of the tunnel. Still they had not come across my head with a dark cloud or a blanket of no hope, when they did I would pull it off as I liked the daylight, I would fight till the day I died, I was innocent and that world had to know it.

I met up with another friend Davey Preston, he was from Page Moss in Huyton and I had known him almost all my life. I knew a lot of his family. We had grown up just around the corner from each other and knew each other through football. He was another football fanatic and played a good game himself, he should have been a professional.

He was doing Eight years at the time for an Armed

Robbery, I had seen him when I was in Walton prison but did not expect to bump into him here. I was pleased to see him and we shook hands and he asked if I needed anything, he was a good lad and had a lot of respect because he could keep his mouth shut.

He was a year younger than me, he was only twenty-one. He came from a big family, it felt good to see him. He was a bit shocked to know I had got twelve years and he knew I had been fitted up and framed, he said to have a look around and see how many people were innocent, he said if you was on the outside looking in you would not believe that it could possibly happen.

He was right, as in the prison you could see it clearly but on the other side you would not dream of what was going on. An old man with a baldy head dressed in a dark blue boiler suit went scuttling passed in front of us as we walked. I asked what the hell was that and sort of giggled, Davey said it was one of the fraggle's (that meant Head Case, in these type of prisons there is a lot of patients, they are known as the mentally not well group, backward people. Dangerous without medication.) and that fraggle in particular was one known as John Straffen.

He had been in prison for years, he was the longest serving prisoner in the country, they'd sentenced him to hang but the queen had given him a reprieve. He was the walking dead. He had killed little girls but because he was mentally retarded he was lucky not to be dead with his head through a noose.

Davey explained that in Long Lartin you get lots of privileges but the down side was that you should not hit the bacons (they were the sex offenders). If you did you were out and in a shity prison far away. So every one must ignore them and carry on with their own thing.

He pointed out some big muscle bulging meat heads to me and told me each one was a sex offender of the highest ranking, I was shocked as some of them were massive, they would have snapped me in half. All doing excessive amounts of prison with nothing to loose, I said it was definitely not the place to go walking in the dark on your own at night. God help me if there was a power cut.

There was also a strange girl that wandered about the prison called Wendy, she would strut her stuff visiting all the wings of the prison, wearing a little tarty mini skirt and handbag over her shoulders. She was a man of course but insisted she was all women and acted like one, even talked like one. She was nuts. I heard she could have a fight as well, she was dangerous to any one who crossed her path or rubbed her up the wrong way.

Well Davey had wised me up some on this place but as I told him I didn't plan on staying too long, I had a private war with the system that I had to attend. Well the weeks passed and the months did to, I was getting restless with no news on the appeal and was getting itchy feet. I had been working out regular in the gym and doing some research into Masonry.

I was talking with a little fat fella who was doing life for murdering his wife, he claimed to be a cousin of the Queen. When I first met him I noticed a hand movement he made and I curiously asked him what it was he had just done. He responded by asking if I was on the Square? I told him I was not on the square but in a vicious little circle. He laughed at my remark and told me that I probably was.

Now I had heard that strange question before and here was the same question again. It took me several weeks of questioning to finally get some answers out of him, he was a Freemason. He explained it all to me but only to a certain degree. I was fascinated and yearned for more knowledge of this mystical secret world that was hidden in our very own society, I went to the library and ordered several books on the subject.

# CHAPTER THIRTY SIX
## MYRA HINDLEY'S LOVER


I was reading the paper one day, the News Of The World. On one of the pages there was a photo of a big North London crime family, their family name was McCann. I scanned all the names with a careful eye and bingo! There was the name Ollie McCann and it was a woman, a dwarf. She was the one who had helped my enemies from Huyton escape to London.

She was very small and had been nicknamed The Poison Dwarf, she had her own sister knee capped with baseball bats. Smashed her legs to pieces. In fact the whole family did not seem like a nice family. They seemed rather vicious and certainly had a big reputation according to the journalist who wrote the article.

One of the cockneys from the wing asked why I had took an interest in the McCann's and I explained the story to him, he went off and re-appeared ten minutes later with a scrap book full of newspaper cuttings. He showed me Ollie McCann for who she really was. He knew the family well and all about them.

Ollie McCann had six children and four of them

were to different fathers. She had done time in prison on a few occasions and was known to have had a string of lesbian lover's, it was no secret. She had been known to inject Heroin. Her present boyfriend John Baldwin was a heroin addict.

It was explained to me that Ollie McCann had ordered the legs of her sister Angie to be smashed in because Angie had exposed the true father of Ollie's eldest daughter Dainty (Elizabeth) to the rest of her family. Which of course would be the right thing to do. The father of Dainty was Crabby; this was Ollie's uncle Jim from Scotland, her father's only brother. It was incest.

Angie had stayed in Scotland with Ollie and knew who the father was but kept it secret. Ollie was only fifteen and Angie a year or so younger. After a silly argument with Ollie, Angie decided to tell the rest of her family that Dainty's dad was Crabby, hence the reason Ollie went into a wild rage and had Angie legs smashed to bits.

He told me she had been Myra Hindley's lesbian lover whilst staying at a woman's prison called Cookham Wood, I was shocked. This was the person that had helped the gang from Huyton escape Liverpool. There was a newspaper article with a photo of Myra Hindley the Moor's Murderess holding a baby. The baby was Gemma, Dainty's newborn daughter. It made me feel ill.

In the North, the screams of Leslie Anne Downey and other children that went missing can still be heard to this day, they will never fade. How could Ollie McCann put her first new born granddaughter in the arms of the worlds worst child killer, how could her daughter Dainty let her new born baby be held in the arms of a monster? A paedophile. How could she? How could any mother in the world glorify a friendship with Myra Hindley the most notorious paedophile of the century?

It makes the saying "Takes One To Know One" come to my mind. Then in the article, Ollie went on to say how Myra Hindley had changed and should be allowed back into the community once again, she had paid her penalty. My god, I would like some of the victims families to bump into her, the woman had to be sick. She was shameful.

Well the cockney also told me exactly what Ollie McCann and her immediate family were all about. They were not a big time criminal organisation with lots of respect like a gangster family at all. They were just a big sick family that bullied people that could not fight back or defend themselves.

They took liberties with weak people to gain a reputation, then frightened the rest of the town with the reputation of their brother Patrick, as he was a top boxer who could have held a title. Anyone who fought back against them would be met with allegations of some sort to discredit them and be paid a visit from the local police wanting to arrest them, for whatever they had done to the McCann family and usually a bit more that they would add on to make sure there was an arrest. They seemed to be Jeckyl and Hyde character's playing the law to their own advantage.

Apparently they worked alongside a copper called Roger Hull, encouraging people to commit crimes and then set them up, they were paid police informers. They were rotten maggots. My cockney friend even told me that Ollie had put her own brother away for ten years and he had not long left that prison, his name was Patrick McCann. I did later catch up with Patrick and he confirmed it all, plus more. What a dirty family they were.

Patrick hated them and I can't blame him, they had manipulated him into burglaring their enemy's homes, they had shown him where and how and then, after he gave them half the money and all the jewellery to sell, they would tell the police. They would give their police friends the inside information, that's how he ended up being under observation by the police for two years.

Treacherous to say the least but that was the way the scum from Harrow made their living, the more bodies traded in the more money they got. It was as if the police had given them a licence to do as they pleased, you get these types of low life's in a lot of areas. Harrow was where they were from. The town was known as Bounty County because of them.

One of Ollie's brother's called Teddy had to pay Ollie dearly. He had taken a lot of stolen jewellery off her and paid her peanuts so, out of spite she had him nicked for handling stolen property and he received a seven-year prison sentence. Ollie also blackmailed Teddy whilst he was in prison for thousands of pounds.

Teddy McCann had been stupid enough to get photographed having sexual intercourse with his male lover Eddy Wright. Ollie his sister got her hands on the photos and ruined his marriage and bank account. The photos were all of a sexual nature in degrading positions with the same male friend.

There was also another fella called knoxy that the cockney told me to speak to, he said that Knoxy from Corby, had a niece whom was a bit simple, retarded. Well, Ollie McCann and her boyfriend had raped her several times together, Knoxy had gone mental. Knoxy had caught them with his niece molestering her, she was only thirteen years of age, he grabbed a chopper from the kitchen and attacked them to save his niece.

He carved Ollie up but, Knoxy ended up getting Eight years for the attack. Whilst Ollie McCann and her boyfriend John Baldwin walked away free with just a few scars to her neck. The niece who was mentally handicapped said she had been raped over seven times including anal rape, was to be deemed as not to be a fit witness. Where is justice?

That was bad, that was sickeningly bad, Ollie McCann was another Myra Hindley in the making. She has to be from the same mould, one for monster's. The Cockney told me that even the town of Harrow itself now had a terrible reputation across the London area as Bounty County because of the McCann's and the inter bred Sweeney's.

Ollie was joined at the hip to the Sweeney's through marriage, the Sweeney's were another big family of similar standing from Harrow. I felt physically sick. The Sweeney's from what I learned were no better themselves, they also had a distinguished reputation for sickness. The McCann's clan consisted of sixteen brothers' and sister's and the Sweeney's of fourteen brothers' and sister's. That was a large amount of people to merge together.

Later on in time the same cockney told me about one in particular called Hughie Sweeney, his friend who was half Greek called Ricky Gayle had been grassed up by Hughie and it was exposed then, Hughie actually went about setting up crimes then tipping the police off.

Hughie also got his own daughter pregnant, yes! Fact. One hundred percent. He fucked his own daughter Joanne and made her abort it when she was fifteen. These were sick people, I felt ill the more I heard about these people. Quite a few of the McCann's and Sweeney's had been accused of sexual offences, rape and being paedophiles.

He told me so many stories about these two families. Each one of them all seemed to have disgusting reputations. I was now gaining lots of information from different quarters about these two very notorious families from London. They were the dirt on the floor. They were the scum of the earth, they were filth. They all seemed to be sexual predators.

There seemed to be more and more stories of the sickening things that these two families had done as I met more people that knew of them, through my time in prison. One of the worse stories was told to me about a fourteen year old boy called Tony Beck, who had ran away from his home, as the kid was a bit mixed up over his parent's separation. The young schoolboy was kidnapped by Ollie McCann and her boyfriend John Baldwin.

They just snatched him off the street and beat the poor little kid up, over and over again for at least a week. They had degraded the little boys mind and stripped him of his clothes and dignity, they then forced him into a bath of freezing cold water for hours tied up and gagged. Threatening him and dangling an electric fire over the bathtub.

The dirty rotten bastards put a piece of bread on the kid's head and let their vicious Rottweiler dog called Jock, scrape the bread off the boy's head with its big paws while he was tied to a chair in the kitchen, bound and gagged crying with fear and begging for mercy.

They mentally fucked the little boy's head up.

No one was prosecuted as the poor little boy did not take his experience to the police or tell his parents of his plight, as he believed in the threats that were made to him. Ollie had told him that she would tell everyone he was a grass if he told anyone. He also feared that his mother would get hurt, as Ollie had told him that if she ever hear's of him again, she would do worse to his mother.

I now had the low down on the whole family from London and I was not impressed. They stood for everything evil and everything rotten. They had a lot of enemies out there. How they have got away with their activities begs belief. They must have been high up, so important to the police that they could not be touched.

No one in the town would prosecute them through fear but like I said, they picked their mark and pushed people who were to weak or to frightened to fight back. Those that did fight back were set up or branded as grass's or sex offender's, they seemed to play on both sides of the fence and used the police to their own advantage.

It seemed that every time the name McCann or Sweeney was mentioned, the villains in the prisons that knew of them would frown, the name was bad. The majority of the McCanns and Sweeney's were all known as informants. I now knew that the so-called friends of my enemies were nothing to fear, I was pleased with my new found knowledge. I would take this scum apart if they crossed my path. They had so many enemies and such a disgusting reputation that I could not believe people had took so much shit off them.

# CHAPTER THIRTY SEVEN
# KICKING THE SYSTEM

My main interest was with the Freemasons, I went back to the library to see if the books I had ordered had come through, they had not. I decided that the progress of the appeal was dithering and my solicitors seemed to be accepting the wait. I'd had enough and told Billy the time for action was here, I was going to go on a hunger strike. Billy decided against it.

I was now on my own and I went for it. I was on hunger strike for five days, it was not long but it caught the attention of the Liverpool Echo and possibly made a ripple or two through the judicial system, as I was booked in straight away for legal visits.

Being on hunger strike was very easy, I had terrorists coming in and telling me to drink lots of water and to lay still as much as possible. It made it easier to get through but it was Hughie Callaghan who sat with me most of the time, he said he would not let me hurt myself. Once it was in the papers he was the first in to tell me it was time to stop, as I had achieved some attention about my situation.

So I stopped and took a week to recover, no harm done. John Hasse had sent Caddy in with a bowl of steaming hot pot and tried to wind me up, as John thought it would get me nowhere doing a hunger strike. He was probably right in one sense as I was not a political prisoner. On the other hand I had to try and try I would.

My mate Davey sent a message for me to see him and told me to come quickly, so I ran over to his wing and saw the chaos with my own two eyes. Charlie Bronson had come out of his cell that morning and decided it was a good day to make a stand. He had put boot polish stripes across his face, all military style and asked if anyone cared to join him and off he went to war, into the T.V. room.

Davey was pissing himself laughing as he pointed to the T.V. room. Charlie Bronson had taken the room under siege and every time a warder got too close he would throw a chair at them but the funniest thing was that the warders started to throw the chairs back at him. It was the talk of the day and Charlie had made yet another stand on his objection to the way the system was run. There was never a dull day with Charlie about.

I saw the Barrister Paul Garlick again and he told me that I was not far away from a hearing but that was only to pass it on to the appeal courts. I was pissed off and wanted something solid. I went back to my cell and decided I would go up on to the roof till I got a date.

Since the last roof top protest, the ways of getting on the roof had been blocked off.

So I sat there one night and decided to paint my cell. I painted it multi coloured and stated my innocence in every colour possible. The cell was a mess I had even painted the ceiling and there was nowhere else to write anything. It stunk of fumes. I also smashed it to bits. The warders come around and were shocked to see the state of the cell with me sitting on the mattress grinning at my masterpiece. It did not go down very well with the Governor, Mr. Owen.

He wanted to know why and I told him that I was innocent, he said I told him that every time he had seen me since the day I arrived there. I said that he must find it difficult to know there was innocent men behind his bars and that if he was a man, he should call the Home Office and tell them that he refuses to keep innocent people in his prison.

He said it was not like that and he could not do so or he would loose his job. I put it to him that he could go to his union officials and see what they could do. He said he could not do that either. I was banging my head against the wall but at least he was listening. He told me I was like a Tooth Ache in his backside, I thanked him for the compliment and spent the next fourteen days in the block, solitary.

Mr. Owen used to threaten me that if I did not behave, he would call my mother at home and tell her I was carrying on like a bad schoolboy. He was not joking as I was allowed to talk to her on the phone now and then and she would tell me that the Governor had been on the phone again complaining about my behaviour.

I was getting to the stage of desperation now and I'd had enough of the promises, I had been in prison now for two and a half years, so I just smashed the cell up. While I was in the block, the warders come for me, it was the Mufty squad, they were the ones who run in and rush you, tie you up and take you away.

I heard one of the inmate's shout that they were here and I knew they were there for me. I quickly threw my T-shirt off and poured baby oil over my body and picked up a pen, I gripped it firmly in my fist. I had enough of these little escapades where they tied me up and give me a belting, this time I would fight. I would give them a nice surprise.

The door burst open but only by two feet as the bed was wedging it closed and the warders could not get right in. I told the first one I would take his eyeball out with the pen and chew the nose off the second one. They froze and backed off. They asked me to calm down and said they were not going to hurt me.

I told them that if they did try again, later on I would get one of them and mutilate them and who, I did not care. They told me I would kill someone if I carried on like this. I replied that if that was the case I would walk out on a technicality because, I should not have been here in the first place as I was innocent and I had been illegally forced into these circumstances.

They seemed to understand, they backed off and left me alone. I was pleased with my little stand against the warders but thought to myself that, maybe I was becoming dangerous. This was not me, I had gone through enough this had to stop, I didn't want to be a nutter or classed as dangerous, what was all this turning me into?

I was told by one of the senior warders that the way I was going I would be either in Park Lane Hospital or end up in Dartmoor Prison. I told him that I didn't give a shit, if they did send me to Park Lane nut house, they would see that the only thing wrong with me was that I was innocent and not sick. So they would just send me back and if they sent me to Dartmoor, I would wreck the place, they would not be able to control me and they too would just send me back.

# CHAPTER THIRTY EIGHT
# BULLARSE AND THE FACTS

I was not too sure how my response would go down but I did have a few sleepless nights thinking of what was said to me. Two days later I was on a day out to Dartmoor. I was on what's known as a "Lay Down" once again to calm me down. I had heard a hell of a lot of bad stories about Dartmoor, I didn't relish the prospect of staying there to long and I did not let on that I was cringing at the thought of being in there.

Well it was a lovely day and it was a great feeling driving down the motorway. We had to drive through a moor to get to the prison and as we got closer it was misty. I couldn't work it out, as it was a hot summers day yet, Dartmoor prison was engulfed in a mist.

It was weird and I could feel an odd sort of atmosphere building up. I took an instant dislike to the place and the ancient looking walls were not a pretty site. Just as we pulled up to the gates I looked at a little old building across the road, it was directly opposite the gates. It was a small building made of flint with a slate roof.

I was attracted to it because there was a sign above the door and on it were the numbers nine, nine, nine, and a picture of an old fashioned tool in the shape of a compass. I found this to be rather strange and the thought of Devil Worshiping came to my mind.

I was taken into the reception area and told to stand on a yellow line, I was to busy trying to take in my new surroundings when I realised I was two meters from the yellow line. The warder looked at me and walked away through a door. I heard a chime, a sort of ding, which I was familiar to by now, it was the riot bell.

Some one must be doing something wrong I thought and carried on doodling around in the reception area. Before I knew it there were around ten warders in the reception area and all were looking at me. I was surrounded and I could feel it.

My first impression was that they were just eyeing me up because I was a long termer, I was wrong. I was grappled to the floor in a neck lock and lifted up in the air. They knew what they were doing and had obviously mastered the manoeuvre, I was like a floppy piece of meat to these lot. I was taken face down as usual to a remote part of the prison and taken into the solitary unit. I was placed on the floor and given a few punches to the head and then I was left alone. They did not mess around in Dartmoor.

I got the impression that they attack first and ask

questions later. I did not have a clue about this place, the walls were visibly wet with damp and it stank. My cell was opened up and there was a team of warders all staring at me through the door, I was getting the feeling that I was in for a good hiding but they had come to stress the new rules to me.

They told me that I must always walk on the white lines in the solitary area and to disobey the rules would lead to a proper good beating. So if I was to stray off the white lines I now knew what would happen. Just for good measure they told me that I would be staying in the solitary unit for a month so that I would understand the rules for sure.

I just stared at them and they all had a kind of hunger in their eyes, for blood, it was written all over their faces that they enjoyed this. I just nodded as if I had heard what they had said and turned away from the door. I did not want to listen to what they had to say I was not interested. This was a pre-historic prison, with pre-historic rules and run by pre-historic animals.

I decided not to have the hourly walk each day and tried not to go out of the cell whatever the excuse, it was humiliating. I was asked if I wanted to go to the library, I went. It was an old room like a cell and quite a few books, I glanced through as many as possible but could not find a fiction one with the last couple of pages in tact.

Obviously some head grinder had taken time out to

make sure there was never an ending to a single fiction book in the library. There is nothing worse than reading a book to find the last few pages missing. I bet you check this now. I noticed some encyclopedias and asked the warder how many books I was allowed to have, he told me six.

I carried the six encyclopedias of my choice to the cell and sat there reading through the lot of them. I even got to read about Masonry. The books were great and I totally enjoyed my newfound knowledge. They were the best books to read, so much knowledge about so many different subjects. I forgot about the world.

Whilst I was in the solitary block I talked through the top of the door to the fella next door. He had told me that the warders were a little bit over the top with force, he explained to me that they were very quick in Dartmoor to attack the convicts and let them know who was in charge.

He went on to explain that he had got himself into a little bit of a temper one day and he shouted back at one of the warders, they soon cooled his temper. They had he said, beat the life out of him and he lost a lung. I could not believe my ears, he told me that they had taken him to a hospital where he had to have one of his lungs removed as it had collapsed.

He mentioned that the warders had put a pillow over his head because he was screaming, he said he did not press charges in case he found himself loosing another lung. It was very disturbing to hear what he was telling me and later on, I got to see his battle scar and a few witnesses that had seen him dragged off verified his story.

It was also stressed to me that when a prison inmate is battered to death or found dead in mysterious circumstances, it seemed that the warders were always found Not Guilty. Warders surrounding the incidents where always sent to Dartmoor. That meant that all the undesirables in the system be it a convict or a warder would be sent to sunny old Devon and out on the moor's to Dartmoor. I was in a dangerous place, a very violent place to state at the least. I tried to keep a low profile and the time came for me to go back to Long Lartin. Or so I thought.

I was not going back I was told and was to be put on one of the wings. I just grit my teeth and got on with it, I did not want them to see that I was disappointed about not returning. I was put on one of the wings in a cell of my own. The walls looked damp inside and out. I met up with a few people I had met on my travels through Winchester.

I was glad to see that there were people that I knew there, they were happy to see me. I was on the exercise yard and talking with a Liverpool lad called Jacko, his real name being Paul Jackson, he was six foot seven, when some fella comes over to me and taps me on the shoulder, it was Joey Bullarse.

I looked at him and said a very strained hello, then he told me he had a few things to tell me. We carried on walking and he told me all he had to say. Apparently he had been asked by the police to tell the court that I had done the Robbery with him and he would receive a very, very extra low sentence.

He told me that he had told the police it was not me or Billy that had done the Robbery with him but, the police did not want to know. He also told me that the police had in fact found forensic evidence belonging to a lad he knew. He was not sure but he thought the forensic evidence came from his friend Tony Millward.

He then said that Brian Peters should never have walked out of court. He had also received a letter telling him that Millward and Peters were involved in a fight with each other in Bournemouth, at the time of the trial. I could only assume why they were fighting but Joey was telling me that the police knew exactly who had done the Robbery.

They even had forensic evidence, which is factual proof! Joey explained that he got no favours getting an Eight Year sentence on a Guilty plea. He was right, he got no favours but, he was telling me that the police did not want to know who had done the Robbery, they just wanted me put away for a long time.

Joey then dropped the bomb shell and told me that the C.I.D. had told him that I had shot a man in Liverpool and would be a walking advertisement for every one in the country to see. Now all would know that you cannot get away with shooting people.

I said to Joey that it seemed to me that no matter what I done, this Robbery was always going to be pinned on me, he agreed. He also told me that he had told his own Barrister to tell my legal team that he was prepared to name the other Robbers in front of the Judge, he said that he got the response that he was not needed by me, he felt that deliberate efforts were made for us not to bump into each other at the trial.

He later showed me letters from his Legal people to prove that they also found it strange that he would not be getting called as a witness. There was also a statement from the forensic laboratory, stating that there had been a forensic test and proved it was not from one of the four that were in custody to begin with.

That was the worse statement he could have shown me, I felt that my legal team must have known and if not, I would be letting them know immediately. I was sickened to see just how low the police had gone, they actually knew who the real Robbers were.

Jacko could not believe what he had heard but he did mention that the whole of the prison population were all talking about the frame up on me. He had heard it everywhere and even warders were known to have talked about it.

Joey introduced me to another fella called Reg Dudley, he seemed a nice old man and was very much a

Londoner. He was Bob Maynard's co-accused. He and Bob had been offered parole but refused it, as they too were innocent! They refused to accept guilt and this meant they could not be released.

They had been fighting for years and could have been out on the street if they admitted their guilt and showed remorse but they couldn't, as they had not done the crime. I was totally amazed by his story. It was shocking what he told me about the system and how he'd seen it. I prayed that I would never be in that situation because I think I would have to leave the prison, one way or another.

I didn't know, I was unsure, I wouldn't know what I would do in their places. It would be one hell of a situation that I sure as hell would not like to be in. I don't think any one would relish the thought. Reg was in a horrible predicament. As I walked about the exercise yard it went dark.

A cloud just plonked itself right on top of the yard. I was amazed, it was a freak of nature. It was explained to me later that it was because we were situated at the top of a hill on the moors and the clouds would often settle on the prison. What a dull place, spooky and the area the prison was situated in was called Princetown. I thought it was all too familiar, this had to be a Devil Worshiping place. I often thought of what the warders must get up to when they are not in work.

# CHAPTER THIRTY NINE
## KUNG FU LIFER

I bumped into Mickey Webb the baldy and his following of a dozen other skin heads all as ugly as each other, no one messed with the baldy's in there, they had it sewn up. They used to make me smile, as I just couldn't believe the way they carried on and dressed.

They all walked with a, 'move out of my way' sort of attitude and they always looked as though they were chewing a piece of some ones ear. I was standing on the wall behind the five a side football pitch, concrete of course with a type of dusty shingle pressed on top of it, if you slid on it you created a dust cloud effect.

Well, on this day we were all lined up behind the goal watching an inter wing football match, I stood on the left of Mickey the skin and around a dozen of his skinhead brothers stood to his right in a long line. All of the prisoners were watching the football and Jacko was playing. He was not hard to miss having legs like a giraffe.

There was one convict walking around with no interest in the football, he was a stocky fella very fit looking and was always in the gym. He was in his mid thirties. He would throw his weight about with the other prisoners and was feared. He was a bully.

He was doing Life imprisonment for murder, he had also raped a female probation officer whilst she visited his former prison. That's why he was sent to Dartmoor, the system could not do much to a person doing Life as he had nothing to loose. He was walking past the goal and as he passed the last skinhead, Mickey gave me a nudge and winked at me.

Mickey then threw a pebble and cracked the Lifer on the back of the head. I giggled and felt that something was going to come of it with all the baldys. I used a towel as a scarf around my neck and had my Donkey jacket on, I tried to sink into it. The Lifer was coming along the queue of skinheads and asking each one individually if they had threw the stone at him, he was getting closer. They all denied it.

He was now on the pavement below, as we were all on the wall a couple of feet higher. He was in front of Mickey and I thought it was going to happen. Mickey said he didn't know anything about the stone and denied all knowledge of it.

I heard the Lifer say something, I looked at him and asked if he was talking to me. I asked him to repeat himself and he did. He wanted to know if it was me that threw the stone. I jumped down and looked him in the face and told him to fuck off away from me and never come near me again, as I did not like or talk to rapists.

His voice growled at me, he said he was a Lifer and he had killed some one with a knife. He made a stabbing gesture at me, I jumped back in case it was a knife in his hand but it wasn't. The atmosphere was electric and the whole of the prison was watching, even the footballers. I knew I had to do something or I would look weak and frightened because I had jumped back away from him.

I also didn't want the Lifer to think that I feared him. So I gave him a left jab, bang on the nose. He went back about five yards and I felt his weight, he was light for a stocky fella. He cursed me and ran at me throwing his hands out like a kung fu fighter and then he jumped up like he was Bruce Lee, to kick out at me.

This time I had no intention of jumping backwards out of his way, I side stepped to the right and jabbed a left to his face, he sort of stopped in his tracks and it was like slow motion, I threw a right cross towards his chin and it landed, with all my weight and force behind it. Bang on the button, I cracked him so hard on the jaw that he was unconscious before he hit the dusty floor on his back.

He was making a snoring noise and his legs were still in the air upright, I looked around and felt like I was in an ancient Roman Arena, a Gladiator and the crowd screamed for his death, I knew I had to finish the fella off. You cannot beat a Lifer, you have to seriously hurt him and make sure he is hospitalised or he will come back and put a blade through your rib cage. I had been schooled at a high level in the prison system and I knew what I had to do.

I looked up at the crowds of prisoners all staring with their mouths wide open and threw away my towel, dropping my Donkey jacket to the floor. The Lifer was stirring and was about to get up, I stamped on his wrist and heard the bones snap. I then stamped on his jawbone and felt his jaw snap, I then done his other arm and one ankle.

He was now screaming with fear and agony, he was saved by one of the Warders from the gym. The warder called me an animal and I don't know why but I held my fists up and said to him that he should come a bit closer and say that. He backed off so I spat down at the Lifer and told him I would kill him, if I seen him again.

I turned and started walking around the yard. It was deadly silence and I felt that none of the prisoners were ever going to argue with me again. I had just coldly taken a Lifer to bits and exposed him for a weak fighter. All the hours of training in the gym had just saved my bacon. I had made it look so easy and had the respect from everyone in the prison.

I continued my walking and the thought of the solitary experience was troubling my mind. I didn't want it but, if the warders were going to take me away I would fight them and turn it into a riot. By the time I had got to where all the warders were standing the yard was again very quiet, a lot of the groups sitting down now stood up, expecting.

It seemed as if every convict was ready to riot if the warders grabbed me. As I walked passed around twenty of the warders in two groups, I tensed myself ready for the fight. I heard a voice say, "was that you fighting before?". I replied that I didn't know what they were on about. To my surprise he said, "that was all I needed to hear."

I felt great, I now knew they were not going to have me. Another warder said it was a lovely day today and another said it was one of the best knockouts he had seen for a long while. I felt so relieved I was not going to solitary again.

The Lifer was helped up to his feet and turned on the warder that had helped him up, so the warder walked away and more or less give the convicts a free reign on the arrogant Lifer. He was set upon by the whole yard and as everyone tried to throw kicks and punches at him, they were hitting other people, within seconds the warders and convicts were all punching out at anyone and everyone. It was like a 'free for all', as the cloudy yard blew up into a dusty fighting arena like something from a gladiator film.

It all settled after a few minutes and the Lifer was carried away to the hospital. When I got back to the wing the warder said my door would stay open all the time and would not be locked whilst he was on the wing working. He then gave me a fag and said how pleased he was that some one had done the Lifer, as the rest of the prisoner's were scared of him.

He had been throwing his weight about and walking down the landings as if he were ten men. He was brought back on to a different wing about a month later and was thrown over the balcony by a few of the inmates. He didn't show again after he was dragged off the steel mesh. It was a very violent prison and the people there only understood violence.

The night of the fight with the Lifer I did not sleep to good, I questioned myself as to the length I had gone to and tried to justify myself and my conscience. It was difficult to be so cold and yet so easy. All I knew was this place and the whole time away had without a doubt changed me into an Evil person, if provoked or pushed into a corner. I would never have beaten a person like the way I beat the lifer, before I was put in prison.

After a couple more months, I was told that I would be going back to Long Lartin, also that my appeal hearing had been listed for December the fourteenth.

# CHAPTER FORTY
## LONG ARMS OF THE MASONS

I was put on a different wing at Long Lartin when I arrived back there. I was also put on the education department and in the Art class. I loved the Art class it was great to see some of the work done in there by the inmates.

There was an Artist in there called Hughie Doherty, he was another Irishman doing a long time, he was in for the Balkham Street Siege in London. He was a very educated man and certainly a man in the know. He used a pallet knife and painted with oils. The work was superb I was intrigued by his professionalism, he was always there with a bit of sound advice for me and I respected him for that. I spent a lot of time with him.

Vince was another Irishman doing a long time and he was the funny one, he took nothing serious and was always laughing. The Art class seemed to be just Irishmen and myself. I got carried away one day deep in thought and used my hands to do a painting. I stood back and tried to see through the colours and the picture, I couldn't, it was a mess and very black, it was done whilst I was in deep thought about the appeal.

Hughie congratulated me and told me all about Van Gough. He said that Van Gough had also painted with his hands and in a sub conscious state. Vince leaned over and told me, all I had to do now was drink a bottle of Absynth and cut my ears off. We all burst out laughing and I screwed it up and put it in the bin.

I knew I had no more concentration or patience to do anything until the appeal was over. Back on the wing I would play cards with a couple of good fellas, Charlie Knight and Alec Sears. They were good company and always told me that this experience would set me in good stead for the rest of my life.

They were very respected within the prison but chose to keep most people at a distance, there were never enough trustable people around. Most of the prison world are one track minded and that's to look after themselves, by any means they can.

The appeal was playing seriously on my mind and what the outcome would be, it made me nervous and on edge. I was only happy when I got a visit. Jeff was still coming to see me and so was my family.

I saw Billy and he was going off his head because Jeff's brother Andrew had been sleeping with Billy's ex wife (he was now divorced). Billy was not amused, as Andrew had been in a argument with her and then decided to take the youngest boy, who was Billy's son Aidy and go off with him. Andrew was reported for kidnapping him, Billy was not amused.

Billy had a go at me and stated he would have Jeff if he sees him on a visit, I would not be his mate if I still accepted a visit from Jeff. I explained to Billy that yes, he had a right to have a go at Andrew but not Jeff. It would be out of order, as Jeff had nothing to do with it.

Well me and Billy did not talk to each other for a while. We see the situation from different angles. When I did speak to him we were in the corridor and who comes up to us but the Governor, Mr. Owen. He said hello and we both returned the pleasantries then Mr. Owen said to both of us, why is it that I am always screaming my innocence and protesting every way how, yet Billy does nothing, but states he to is innocent.

Billy said in a meek and mild voice that he was doing his protesting in his own sort of way. The Governor said to Billy that when he can, let him know what way that is, please do, so that he can make a note of it. Then he told Billy that it was as if he had accepted his plight and looked a good candidate for parole.

I turned, looked at Billy and said to him that he was letting himself down and walked away. I didn't speak to him for quite some time after that, the Governor had a point but, I also knew that Billy was a half beaten young man. I was fighting on my own and Billy knew it. It seemed the closer to the appeal I was getting, the heavier the stress was becoming.

I had been back into the library and enquired about the books that I had ordered about Masonry. They had not been able to get the copies I had ordered on several occasions. I knew that Masonry had something to do with my trial and the entire goings on with the police.

I had learned quite a lot about the secret squirrels in society and just how far they could reach, I wanted answers but I could not get them. I had learned that there is a ladder in Masonry which the individual will climb, each rung of the ladder would be classed as a degree, he would go up to three degrees.

From there it would be his choice to go further or to branch off into the Templar's. One person will ask if one is on the square, the other will answer him by saying he is or he be a Harris, that means his father was or is one, it's a coded chat with fixed answers only known by Masons, also they do not Swear to God, they Swear to the Great Architect in the Sky.

It gets deep and can be a powerful subject, the real beauty of it is Solomon. It gets to be a fascinating topic. It is a very mystical subject and I learned that you would have to be recommended to join by at least two members or you were entitled to join by privilege, that privilege being that you had to have been educated at Grammar School. I was.

I used to stay on Lord Derby's estate and now realised the importance of it. There was a Masons Lodge there and I remember going inside it with the gamekeeper's son to pick up more shot for the days hunt. I had viewed a room with masterful floor decoration.

There was a big secret world out there and they had all the little funny handshakes and sported the Onyx rings but, I couldn't use it as a defence as I had no positive proof. I came back from the library one day and I was called into the office, a senior warden wanted to talk to me. I asked him what he wanted me for and he closed the door behind me.

He asked me why I wanted the Masonry books. I told him that I was interested in the subject. He told me that he was not soft and that if I were to go out on the appeal and dirty the name of Masonry in connection with my conviction, it could hold serious consequences. I asked him if he was threatening me and he said no. He was, it was a veiled threat.

He told me that it was not the Masons who had put me away but certain individuals who could very well have tried to use their powers as practicing masons, to influence the case against me. I made a sign to him by putting my left hand across my eyebrow as if looking into the distance and swiping my right hand down across my body, in a fashion done by the trial prosecution to the Juror acting as Foreman.

The Senior Warden looked at me in disbelief, he was horrified I had used a sign from a very high up degree. I then asked did he have anything else to say.

He asked where I had learned the knowledge of Masonry and I told him I could not say but I told him that that gesture was one of a Mason in dire straits, it was a sign of distress and must be acknowledged by all brothers that could see, it was the S. O. S. of the Brotherhood.

He carried on trying to justify the Brotherhood and swore to me that for my own sake, I should not pursue that line and shed no blame on his organisation. I knew I was right, the police had used Masonry to get me put away, they had abused their power of being Mason's and in turn crucified me. I often wandered how that senior warden knew that I was indirectly accusing the Masons, was it on my file in the office or was it just a known fact. Masonry is shrouded in a veil of secrecy, which makes it more inviting to be on the inside.

All the same it clearly is stated in their own sworn testaments that the power you obtain is not to be abused in favour for ones wrong doings, so the police in my case had obviously broken their own rules, that is what I have read and believe to be true. It was my job now to knock these offenders off the rungs of their ladder.

# CHAPTER FORTY ONE
## Q.C. WITH A FRIENDLY HANDSHAKE

I was given a legal visit and told that a Q.C. would be representing me at the court of appeal in London. I would also be getting produced at the courts. This is very often done in your absence and not many convicted people attend the court. The Q.C. would be flying home to England to deal with the case personally.

He was in Hong Kong presently representing a company called Marconi, it was a ten-month trial but he had found a date to come over and would spend Xmas in England, he had apparently put himself out to represent me.

I felt something mysterious going on, these Q.C.s at that sort of level did not come cheap and Legal Aid would not cover it. The Q.C. was called David Jeffrey's, it all sounded good and very promising, my hopes were now building up. I was to meet him two days before the appeal hearing. I was more nervous than ever.

It seemed all of a sudden that I was getting visits from all different sources. I was called on to a visit and a young lady introduced herself to me as being from a

T.V. program called Rough Justice. She was really positive and explained that there was nothing they could do at the moment but, if my appeal was to fail it would be different. They would like to interview me and do a documentary about my plight, she wanted a signed agreement and I told her, no problem. I was willing to do anything to prove my innocence.

She knew about most of the evidence and was horrified by the court proceedings at the trial. I also gave her permission to read and copy my file at the solicitor's office. She was very warm and told me that they would do everything in their power to see I was released, she even knew about the forensic reports of another person being involved in the Robbery, which proved in her mind that it could not have been me.

I spent the whole morning with her and went through all the points with her, it was like a breath of fresh air and I felt that things had to happen now. She told me that she had been to see my mother at home and that she had spent a few days with her going through the paperwork that she had.

I come to the conclusion that her program would not entertain just anybody screaming their innocence but a case with merit, they would expose it on national T.V. It gave me comfort to know that I had something really positive to fall back on if I was to fail on the appeal. She also told me that she had passed the case through her legal team for the program and they were astonished that the only evidence was an Identification of a pair of eyes.

There was nothing else. She told me to keep my spirits up and keep on believing that I would walk free soon enough, she would have national exposure within three months on prime time T.V. if the appeal failed. I told her I would prefer to win the appeal and stay anonymous, try and get my life back but if not I would go on their program. I said my farewell and she wished me luck for the appeal. It was really something to know that I was being looked after by people that could do something positive. I thanked my mother for that.

My mother had fought long and hard amongst all the difficulties she was going through. She had turned up at Temple in London and demanded the attention of the judicial society and screamed at them not to let her son be lost in the system, she let them know that there was a voice outside telling them day in and day out that innocent boys were locked away for a crime they did not do.

My mother even held a protest outside the Houses of Parliament and soon got the interest of an M.P. called Sean Hughes. He decided to make waves after what he see in evidence, he was disgusted and wrote to me on several occasions telling me he had badgered the upper tiers of Parliament for a fair hearing.

Things seemed to be looking good, my mother just wouldn't stop hassling and harassing people until she was heard and noted. A police commissioner threatened her with Prison on one occasion. The commissioner had said his men would not frame a human in a court of law but, he did not have a lot to say when my mother confronted him with evidence that contradicted his statement. She had proof that her son was framed and spoke out about it. The cage was rattled. My mother, for speaking out was almost put in prison.

My mother was practically out of her mind with the worry and the stress of it all, she did not deserve to be going through this. None of us did. She had tried almost every thing a person could try to expose the situation and now it was left in the hands of the gods.

There was nothing else we could do. It would now be up to David Jeffrey's. I kept on wondering to myself how, I was to be represented by him. I knew it had to be someone with money, a lot of money behind it. My mind played overtime with itself and I came up with a few conclusions.

On the fist hand my parents may have re-mortgaged their home to pay. On the second, I knew my mother's sister was married into Paul McCartney's family and were close to Paul. I remember meeting Paul and the rest of the Beatles when I was a kid, at Auntie Gin's house in Dinhas Lane, I also knew that Paul McCartney was not the scrooge that people in Liverpool were led to believe he was.

He was far from it, I know that he had ploughed a

lot of money into the City, trying to help people without his name being used. He told me when I was sixteen that he would finance anything I wanted to do, as long as it was in the music game but I was never to go into the music world. I understood how he worked and I used to cringe when people would slag him off for being a scrooge, I knew differently and I am sure a lot of other people know what I am saying is quite right.

So, he was a possibility or someone close to him, yet there was still another. Owen Oysten, now this was another fella that was not recognised for his kindness. He was of great wealth and a gentleman to go with it. He had made his own fortunes and seemed to step in for the common man when needed, for example; When the Liverpool F.C. supporters were arrested at the Belgian Heysel Stadium on the continent and charged with riotous behaviour, who stepped in and put their bail monies up and the legal expenses? yes Owen Oysten. He did not ask for the publicity and praise for his good deed, he remained anonymous and spent his own money.

So here I was just wondering how had my Q.C. been paid for, was it just true grit from a normal hard working family or was it one of the famous multi millionaire Godfather's of Liverpool, or was it another Godfather from Liverpool with the cash to put the system back in line and wanting to keep his anonymity. I did not know and will probably never know.

All I do know is that my mother gets the credit,

she done me proud and suffered herself to see that I was not a forgotten case, shoved under the carpet like so many others. It was not over yet though by a long way, I had seen so many bad things happen in court cases and was not one to have faith in the system.

I had seen men do fifteen years of prison and they were innocent, there was not just one or two, there was plenty. I did not want to be on that pile so I knew the appeal had to be right, I just didn't have the heart to carry on for years screaming about it, I would take drastic measures if the appeal were not to succeed and escape was first on the list.

I met with David Jeffrey's a few days before the appeal hearing and the two of us spent the morning together. He was tall and had longish hair with streaks of grey, a pleasant face with strong features but a warmth about him and full of self-confidence. I liked him instantly and the more he spoke the more I liked him.

We did not entirely discuss the whole case, he wanted to know what I would do if I was released, I told him I had not let it cross my mind and that I would probably just seek a bit of quiet somewhere until my head was adjusted to society's way of life. I just didn't know, as I was to scared to think that way. I had thought like that before and I was mentally knocked by the Guilty verdict.

He said he could understand and asked about the

compensation issue. I told him I was not interested in compensation at all. I just wanted to be home and see my family again, the thought of the money had never crossed my mind either.

He didn't want to say too much about the outcome of the hearing but he did say that from what he had read and seen so far, he didn't see me losing the appeal, he said worst way it will last three days.

I told him I did not want empty promises so he said he would promise me that he would use everything possible, to make sure the Judges could see the wrong doings and the lack of evidence used that should have been used. Also the fact that there was forensic evidence showing others had done the Robbery.

I liked him, he shook my hand and I felt a small surge of pressure through one of his fingers between my knuckles, I looked at him and said that at least now, I had got some one on the square in my corner. He laughed, the next time I was to see him was at the appeal courts. I felt confident but, not that much, I was to scared to feel sure, I had been through some strange times and was very wary to trust in the system but I was hopeful.

# CHAPTER FORTY TWO
# THE FIRST APPEAL HEARING

The day before the appeal I along with Billy was taken to Wandsworth prison over night. We were put in the same cell and we made our differences up, he was in a panic and terrified to death that it would all be a repeat performance of the trial at Winchester.

We both discussed the possibilities of what could happen and it was always back to the same old push, I would walk and I would win the appeal, we were both determined that this time we would not be silent but the same old scary feeling creeped back in to our heads, what if it all went wrong? What if it was all false like a big show? After all it is hard for the courts to release people and state that they were wrong to put them in prison. This was a catch twenty-two for the Judiciary. I hardly slept that night.

Next morning we were took to the central Criminal Courts of Appeal in London. My nerves were gone I was not myself and I was in a permanent sweat, Billy looked very white himself. This was going to be the biggest day of our lives. We were put into a big cell and told that we would be in court very soon.

It was less than ten minutes before we were called up. I had paced the floor of the cell and not spoke a word, I had not a lot of speech left and I was not in the mood to talk I just walked around in circles in the cell. Billy seemed to be tongue tied as well. We were taken into a corridor and told that we would be in court Seven.

I was pleased, as it was my lucky number. We were taken through a door and I was told to enter first, I did and sat down, then Billy sat on my left. I was in a sort of bird box high up on the wall almost at the same level as the Judges, I could see down into the court, it was very eerie and strange. The atmosphere was a totally electrically charged one. I felt a pressurised feeling in the courtroom.

The actual courtroom was built in the sixteen hundreds I guessed and could see that everything in it was original. I felt as though I was taken back in time hundreds of years and wondered to myself, who had sat in this very seat and been sentenced to death by execution. What famous people in history have had to sit here previously. This was the highest court a person could go to, it was terrifying.

To my left were the three Judges all old of age but the one in the middle being more senior than the other two, he had one to his right and one to his left. He the main Judge in the middle was called, Lord Justice

McCowan.

He reminded me of a proper Lord on his throne holding the Scales Of Justice, the two other judges being one for the positive and the other for the negative, there was a sort of balance. To my right and down were all the Q.C.s and their legal teams, behind them were the C.I.D. Further over to the back was all my family and friends, a few reporters and a few of Billy's friends. I was praying to god that I would do anything god asked if he would make them choose the right decisions. I could not move, I felt paralysed in my seat.

The case began with a quick summary of the Robbery by the prosecution and it was to my ears a pathetic summary, it was as if the prosecution Q.C. had lost his bottle and was on the retreat, there were no suggestion of me actually being a Robber, just that my eyes were pointed out by one of the victims from the Robbery and that was it.

I thought they were cowards and had a lot more to say in the presence of Judge Lewis McCreery, they had brandished me as an Evil Sadistic Brutal Bastard at Winchester Crown Court. Now here they were, like mice before a Law Lord. I felt a rush of excitement as my Q.C. took to the stand. This was my last shout of defiance and the very last crack at the whip to prove my innocence.

I was sitting and actually shaking in the pigeon box Billy was to, we both sensed something here and maybe it would be Justice, just maybe. My Q.C. outlined the case and the witnesses that had not been used in the defence, he also went on to state that Jackie Kelly would also appear along with the witnesses, she being a prosecution witness that exposed the actual police wrong doings and was now a defence witness.

He then stated that the Judge Lewis McCreery, had deliberately misled the Jury at the trial and mis-directed them into believing that the men on trial were guilty. He named just less than seventy points on the Trial Judges summing up alone.

He was about to carry on and explain the police factors and how strange the facts were, that there was even forensic evidence, hidden from the defence that proved beyond doubt that there was someone other than the men accused. He was cut short. The main Law Lord asked Billy's Q.C. if he was going down the same road, he said he was and mentioned that he also had Perjury accusations to put forward against the police. The Law Lord asked the court to retire for one hour.

I was stuck in my seat and couldn't move it was riveting stuff right there in front of my own two eyes and my fighter's were going for the kill, they were like vicious dogs with lock jaw around the prosecutions throat. They were not letting me swing.

I felt that there was to be justice but why should the Law Lords stop the case in mid flow without hearing any of the evidence. I was scared, very scared. We were taken back to the cell again and Mr. Jeffrey's came in to see me, he was smiling. I asked him what was going on and he explained that the Law Lords would make a decision on whether or not the evidence could be used, as the appeal court was just about points of law.

In other words they could say, "No,, we cannot use it as it was available at the trial and should have been used then." He said it was odd that the Law Lords had stopped the appeal for one hour as they usually hear it all, then make decisions. He told me to have faith he was not done yet, I smiled and thanked him for everything he was doing and I meant it.

He was fighting for my life and he was showing it. I was sat back in the cell and it was Billy who was pacing the floor now, every time he looked at me he giggled and said that, at last there was nothing hidden here and there were no lies. I giggled too, but really we were both giggling with nerves.

We were called back to the court and this time we were shaking like leafs. We sat down again and the court was in silence, I put my head down and waited. The Law Lord in the middle spoke and broke the silence of the court.

He said he had heard enough of the applications and had studied the summing up of the trial by the Judge at Winchester. He then said they had come to a decision, they were now going to reserve their right for Judgement, which they would pass a week later. That was it, what the hell was that supposed to mean?

I was shocked and mystified by the words he said. They had heard enough? There was a lot more to go, what was going on? I left the court and was put back in the cells with Billy, both our heads firmly on another planet. We were totally bewildered. Was it good or was it bad?

My Q.C. was there to see me again and he was as puzzled as I was, he said he could not determine an outcome or predict their thoughts but he said to me it was a good sign that I was to be produced in a weeks time, before them again. As he left the room he winked and asked what would I drink if he took me for a pint next week.

# Man fighting to prove his innocence

A MAN alleged to have taken part in a sadistic armed raid on a Southampton public house will have to wait to learn if his bid to clear his name has proved successful.

Anthony John Allen, 24, was alleged to have been one of three men who burst into the living quarters of the Seaweed Inn in Weston Lane, Southampton, three years ago.

Local publican, Mr Ronald Bannister, was beaten with a club and his wife and barmaid were threatened with knives.

Three appeal judges late yesterday reserved their decision in the appeal by Allen, currently serving a 12-year jail sentence.

The Liverpool man was convicted of robbery after a trial at Winchester Crown Court that ended on February 23 last year.

The sadistic raid against the sleeping landlord and his wife was condemned by a judge at the time as "evil and sadistic".

At the appeal hearing Allen's counsel, Mr David Jeffreys told judges that the attack at the Seaweed was "horrible" and there must have been a powerful temptation for the jury to convict the men in the dock.

He added that the identification evidence was not strong and that the trial judge's directions to the jury had been faulty.

THE
coas
hom
of pe
But
floodir
the ea
recede
died d

# CHAPTER FORTY THREE
# ROYAL MAIL HAND DELIVERED

I went back into the cell and Billy felt that this could be it but, we were both scared to build up our hopes, it's easy to do so and when it comes back with a wrong conclusion you are devastated and I don't think we could take any more devastation in our lives. We were not allowed to have any visits at the courts so we were taken back to Long Lartin on a transit bus with windows.

The warders were from Long Lartin and had stayed over night, they had also listened to the proceedings and were of the opinion that we were to be released soon. They told us that we may not go back to court in a hurry but if we did, then they would receive a letter very soon at the prison.

The warders joked with us about their night out and said sincerely that they thought in their own opinions, we were innocent and hoped we would be set free. They had never believed it until they heard with their own ears today what had gone on. We got back to the prison late and went straight to our cells. I crashed out and did not wake till eleven thirty the next day.

I was woken by the guard that had took me to the appeal courts and he was trying to shake me awake, I asked what was wrong and he was grinning from ear to ear saying, "look what I have got for you." He held a letter with a thick wax seal on the back, it was addressed to me. I asked him who was the letter from? He told me only the likes of Royalty wrote and sealed their mail, it was from the Law Lords, a Queen's messenger delivered it by hand.

I tried to take it all in. I held the envelope sitting up and looked over it. I rubbed my eyes and said I would open it, slowly, the warder was as excited as myself. I opened it up and read the words aloud, it stated that I must produce this warrant before my jailor and he shall see fit that I will be at the Court Of Appeal on the twenty first of December there would be no excuse for me not to be there.

The warder jumped up and said a big Yes! He grabbed my hand and told me I was going home. He said they would not produce me at court unless I was being released. He knew I was appealing against conviction and not the sentence so it was not to slash the lengthy years off the sentence.

I didn't know what to think I was rattled and felt spooky, the warder asked if I fancied a cup of tea and of he went to put the kettle on. At the time I must have been asleep but, I was now waking up to the facts. This was a live dream, a letter hand delivered to my cell this quick and unopened.

The warder was back with the tea, he was alright and I got on well enough with him, we called each other by first names, that was the difference with the dispersal prisons, they were humane and half civilised compared to the likes of Dartmoor.

His name was Andy, he had played football at West Ham some year's back, we had something in common and we always spoke about football. He asked what I would do if I was released and I told him that I was a bit scared to think or take it for granted that I would be released. He agreed but insisted that if I did get out that I should consider playing football at a professional level. He had contacts that would put me in the right direction. He had watched me play several times and was impressed, he was serious so I told him if I did consider it, I would call him at the prison when I had settled.

The thought of being out in the big world would not come into my imagination, I would not let it. I was too frightened in case I was refused and had to stay in prison for years to come. I did not trust in the system after my experiences and I was not about to get my head focused on being released.

That week of waiting passed so slow and a couple of days before I was due in court, the Governor Mr. Owen, came to see me. He wished me all the best and told me he would be glad to see the back of me in a nice way. He hoped the courts would get it right this time shook my hand and left. I felt honoured that he should do that.

The next morning I came down the stairs to make my way to reception and a lot of inmates from the prison came over to shake my hands and wish me luck, I felt that all these people were genuine and I felt they truly believed I was to be freed. I thanked all them people, as I needed that bit of assurance.

I had taken it to the wire with my protesting. There was nothing left I could do, to prove to the world that I had not done the crime. I was innocent.

# CHAPTER FORTY FOUR
# THE ROYAL COURTS OF JUSTICE

I sat silently on the way to the appeal courts and the warders asked me not to do a runner and took my handcuffs off. That was weird and it meant to me that this time I was the favourite to win. I was thinking to myself that Cyril Burkett, the bookie on the wing, would be taking bets on my case, I wondered what my odds would be.

We got to Wandsworth again and we were given the Red Carpet treatment by the warders They walked us to our cell and made everyone get out of our way declaring that two free birds are on their way through. We was the talk of the prison, all kinds of different convicts were coming to the cell asking us if we were really innocent and was we really doing twelve years and eleven years.

It was so strange, we were not ordered to do anything, just asked if we wanted this or wanted that, the attitudes from the warders was unbelievable. We did not sleep that night and sat for the majority of it in silence, it was a time of reflection and wonder. We were finally here after three long horrible and torturous years of anguish and mental onslaught. We had made it to the finishing line, or was it to be the road into hell.

I looked into a mirror and thought of how much I had changed, I could now shave regular and I also had a lot of grey hairs on my head, I looked year's older than I really was. I looked like a man now, not a kid no more. Time had certainly taken its toll on my image in the mirror. I felt my youth had been taken away from me. I was Olympic fit and had gained weight up to eleven and a half stone, I was solid. I also knew I had developed a vicious streak in me that was ever so cold and brutal.

I suppose that if you live within an animal kingdom, you have to fit into the realm, or the others around you would eat you. It's the law of the Jungle. I wondered if I was ready for the world without bars or would the world be ready for me? I didn't know what to think so I just dreamed on, thinking of anything and trying not to think of the outcome at tomorrows hearing.

It was like before and we were taken to the appeal courts. We were back in my favourite numbered court, Seven. I said thanks to the main man upstairs in the sky. I did not get to see my Q.C. and waited patiently for three hours before we were called into the court.

I walked in to the bird box as before and Billy followed, the rush of blood I could feel pumping at tremendous pace through my body was like never before. I could even feel the throbbing of my pulses and hear my own heart beat pumping away.

I quickly looked around to see who was in the court, I caught my mothers eyes, I nodded and smiled to her, she was holding her Rosary Beads to her chest and mouthing a prayer to the lords, I could see the fear in her eyes but recognised a bit of hope there. I was hoping that this would be quick, I was very warm and I was sweating fiercely.

The Gavel went down and the court was enveloped in a deadly silence. The Law Lord explained to the court that he had reserved his Judgement for this day, as he was not happy with the trial courts actions. He explained that it was inexplicable what had happened to the accused and told me to stand up.

He told me I was free to go! I fumbled to move but my legs would not move, Billy had grabbed my legs, the Law Lord must have noticed and told Billy to stand, he did and grabbed my arm, he was free to go as well!

The Law Lord carried on with his Judgement but I could not hear the words, there were a few screams of delight heard in the courtroom and as I looked, I could see Jeff poking his finger into Essary's face telling him he was going to go down, for framing us. I just stumbled to the door with Billy but, we were like pieces of jelly falling over each other trying to get through the courtroom door in case they changed their minds.

The Law Lord carried on with his Judgement as the

commotion carried on in the court. We had gone. The warders were all patting us on the back and our personal belongings were in bags by the metal gate waiting for us. The warders asked if we would like dinner first and we all burst out laughing. The door was opened and the warders told us to follow the corridor.

We did at a running pace half expecting the police to jump on us. It was dark in the corridor but, as we reached the end and turned the corner the bright light of the day hit our eyes, the fresh cold air hit our faces and there was the smell of the real world, freedom at long last. We were now free and back into the world.

Our families and friends ran to us and we all spent ten minutes hugging and kissing each other, the women were crying tears of joy, we all seemed to have tears in our eyes and it certainly was a beautiful moment. Someone shouted to all go in the pub across the road so we all made for the pub. I just followed every one else, I was on cloud cuckoo and the buzz was just total ecstasy.

My Q.C. had a pint of lager waiting for me on the bar, I shook his hand and took the pint, there was a big cheer all around as I lifted my glass, both myself and Billy clinked our glasses together and the cheer's were even louder.

The beer made me a bit dizzy. I felt a magical feeling all over. What a long hard journey I had just been on. I didn't need the beer, I was on a unique and super natural high. I then sat down and held my mothers hand, she was still crying, was still shaking. I told her it would be ok now and kissed her cheek, it was the happiest I had ever seen her in my life.

# 'Evil eyes' man freed

A MAN jailed for 12 years for robbery after one of the victims picked him out at an identity parade because of his "frightening, evil and sadistic eyes" was cleared by the Court of Appeal in London today.

Three judges freed Mr Anthony John Allen, 23, of Huyton, Liverpool, and also cleared 23-year-old Mr William Willis who had been given an 11-year sentence for his alleged part in the attack three years ago on a Southampton publican, his wife and a barmaid.

The judges ruled that the convictions were unsafe because of "serious and fundamental" errors by Judge Lewis McCreery in his summing up to the jury at Winchester Crown Court.

Lord Justice McCowan said Mr Allen, Mr Willis and a third man who pleaded guilty, all staying at a woman's flat in Copenhagen Towers, Southampton, were alleged to have threatened the victims with knives after breaking into the Seaweed Inn in Weston Lane.

Page 315

# EPILOGUE

It so happened that the police involved with the wrong doings in my case were demoted and sent off to different areas with lower ranks.

The Animal himself Judge Lewis McCreery was asked to resign in a formal way, he did so and was never to practice his trade again.

I never felt Justice was done but, I hope the police involved have something coming to them, each time they feel fate has landed them a bad deal. I hope they picture me smiling at them. I will haunt them forever, as they done to me for three long dangerous and torturous years. I would like to get into their minds, even their dreams, I shall never forgive them.

They put an innocent boy into an evil world, sadistically, which would obviously have a life long effect on his life.

What become of me? Don't worry, I will tell you in my own words. It's all in Volume Two.

**www.innocencetoevil.co.uk**